MODERN AMERICAN HUMOUR

'The best of them are all here, from Dorothy Parker to Art Buchwald. And, of course, with the drawings—Gluyas Williams, Thurber and Steinberg.'—*Star*

'Here is humour that is slick, polished, broad, punchy, irresistibly Transatlantic. Here, for good measure, is a delightfully inconsequential introduction by Bernard Braden which sets the laughter-ball rolling.'—*Manchester Evening News*

THE PHOENIX BOOK OF
MODERN AMERICAN HUMOUR

Chosen and Presented by
MICHAEL BARSLEY

With an Introduction by
BERNARD BRADEN

PAN BOOKS LTD : LONDON

First published 1956 by Phoenix House, Ltd.
This edition published 1959 by Pan Books Ltd.,
8 Headfort Place, London, S.W.1

FOR SARAH AND
MARGARET

Printed in Great Britain by Richard Clay and Company, Ltd.,
Bungay, Suffolk

CONTENTS

And drawings by GLUYAS WILLIAMS (page 123)
JAMES THURBER (pages 124 and 125), and SAUL
STEINBERG (pages 126 and 127).

ACKNOWLEDGMENTS

Thanks are due to the following for permission to reprint copyright material:

The author and Messrs Hamish Hamilton Ltd for 'The Secret Life of Walter Mitty', from *The Thurber Carnival*, 'The Night the Ghost Got In', from *My Life and Hard Times*, 'The Lady on the Bookcase', from *The Beast in Me and Other Animals*, and for the drawings on pages 124–5, by James Thurber; Messrs Doubleday & Co. Inc. and Faber & Faber Ltd for *cheerio my deario* and *pete the parrot and shakespeare* by Don Marquis; the author and Messrs Jonathan Cape Ltd for the extract from *Gentlemen Prefer Blondes* by Anita Loos; Mrs Milt Gross for 'Ferry-Tail from Keeng Mitas' from *Nize Baby* by Milt Gross; Messrs Alfred A. Knopf Inc. and Chatto & Windus Ltd for 'Father Wakes Up the Village' from *Life with Father* by Clarence Day; the J. B. Lippincott Company for 'Blood Pressure' from *More than Somewhat* by Damon Runyon (copyright, 1930, by Damon Runyon); Messrs J. M. Dent & Sons Ltd for 'The Cliché Expert Testifies on Love' from *Sullivan at Bay* by Frank Sullivan; the Viking Press Inc. and Penguin Books Ltd for 'Entrance Fee' by Alexander Woollcott; Messrs Harper Brothers and the Benchley Estate for 'Sporting Life in America: Dozing' from *One Minute Please* by Robert Benchley; the author, the Viking Press Inc. and Messrs Methuen & Co. for 'You Were Perfectly Fine' and three poems from *The Best of Dorothy Parker*; Messrs A. M. Heath & Co. Ltd for 'Mr Kaplan the Magnificent' from *The Education of Hyman Kaplan* by Leonard Q. Ross; the author, the Viking Press Inc., and Messrs John Lane The Bodley Head Ltd for 'No Trouble at All' from *Small Beer* by Ludwig Bemelmans; Messrs J. M. Dent & Sons Ltd for 'The Turtle', 'Biological Reflection', 'Oh, did you get the Tickets?', 'Reflections on Ice-breaking', and 'Home, 99 44/100% Sweet Home' by Ogden Nash; Messrs Dodd, Mead & Co., the authors, and Messrs Constable & Co. Ltd for the extract from *Our Hearts Were Young and Gay* by Cornelia Otis Skinner and Emily Kimbrough; Messrs Rinehart & Co. Inc. and Dennis Dobson Ltd for 'How to Swat a Fly' from *How to Attract the Wombat* by Will Cuppy; the author and the Editor of *The New Yorker* for 'Shakespeare, Here's your Hat' by Wolcott Gibbs; the author and Messrs Reinhardt & Evans for 'Waiting for Santy' and 'Strictly from Hunger' by S. J. Perelman; the author and Messrs Faber & Faber Ltd for 'It's Wonderful to be a Mother' from *I Lost my Girlish Laughter* by Jane Allen; Messrs John Farquharson Ltd for 'The Sleepy Piano-player' from *Looking for a Bluebird* by Joseph Wechsberg; Messrs Alfred A. Knopf Inc. and Messrs Michael Joseph Ltd for 'The Inside Story' from *Natural History of Nonsense* by Bergen Evans; Messrs Martin Secker & Warburg Ltd for the extract from *The Pajama Game*, originally published as *A Gross of Pyjamas*, by Richard Bissell; Messrs William Heinemann Ltd for the chapter from *I Married the World* by Elsa Maxwell; the author and Messrs Chatto & Windus Ltd for 'The Party Watchers' from *Art Buchwald's Paris* by Art Buchwald; 'Captive Audience' (copyright, 1953, by Fantasy House Inc.) by Ann Warren Griffith is reprinted by permission of the author and *The Magazine of Fantasy and Science Fiction*. The drawing on page 123 is reproduced by permission of Gluyas Williams and the Editor of *The New Yorker*; those on pages 126-7 from *The Passport* by permission of Saul Steinberg and Messrs Hamish Hamilton Ltd and Harper Brothers.

Every effort has been made to trace the owners of copyright material. Should any acknowledgment have been inadvertently omitted it will be included in any future edition.

INTRODUCTION

by Bernard Braden

THIS IS the page I usually skip when I begin to read a book, because a good book is self-sufficient. This is a good book, so you might as well turn the page now.

If, perversely, you've decided to stay with me, the reward will be negligible. Mr Barsley has insured himself against attack by pointing out that his choice of humour is purely personal, and almost all the writers he seems to like are people of formidable talent and reputation. I like them too, which only proves that Mr Barsley and I enjoy a similar taste in American humour.

As a Canadian, I could have wished for the inclusion in this collection of the late Stephen Leacock and the far-from-late Eric Nicol. It may be that Mr Barsley plans a subsequent book of Canadian humour, but I doubt it. This was tried once in Canada, but when the volume was assembled the covers proved to be too close together. Since then, the occasional Canadian humorist has managed to sneak into the less reputable anthologies of American humour on the flimsy excuse that, strictly speaking, Canadians are American, too. Last year an Argentinian almost made it on the grounds of being South American, but he was yanked out because they found out in the nick of time that he was really an Iroquois Indian with a forged passport. Still, in an effort to be mildly controversial, I'd like to go on record as saying that, in my opinion, Eric Nicol has written much funnier pieces than either Elsa Maxwell or Art Buchwald. So there.

Mr Barsley makes no apology for including writings from the nineteen-twenties as 'modern', and if he needs corroboration for that opinion I can offer him the authority of Mark Twain, who maintained that while humour must not profess to teach, and must not profess to preach, it must do both to live forever. And by 'forever' he said he meant thirty years.

I commend this book to you with all my heart, but don't take my word for it. Let the last word be with Josh Billings, an American humorist who died in 1885. He said, 'There is very few judges of humour, and *they* don't agree.'

So you see, you're on your own. I *told* you to skip this page.

BERNARD BRADEN

FOREWORD

IT IS MORE than thirteen years since I last attempted to gather a collection of American Humour. Much has happened since then to the lighter side of American Life. The *New Yorker* has attained its silver jubilee, but the death of its unique and remarkable founder, Harold Ross, and the rising popularity of television and advertising have led to an alteration in the status of the American humorist, as a writer and artist.

When James Thurber, in 1952, broadcast a talk for the BBC Third Programme on American Humour, he pointed to the dearth of new writers for the printed page. 'In the last twenty years' he said, diffidently and awkwardly (like his own Walter Mitty, up against the wall and facing the firing squad), 'I could name, on the fingers of one hand, the new writers and the new humour that have come along.' His explanation? The absence of 'the quiet mind and the tranquil spirit which mean most to the creation of humour'.

Thurber is something of an elder statesman. He did not always feel this way about humour. In his *My Life and Hard Times* he analysed the humorous writer as one 'who has, nobody knows why, a genius for getting into minor difficulties . . . to call such persons humorists is to miss the nature of their dilemma and the dilemma of their nature. The little wheels of their invention are set in motion by the damp hand of melancholy . . .'

I have been given the whole-hearted indulgence of my publisher in choosing those authors and excerpts which I myself consider amusing. This is not a representative collection, and I am always finding myself going back to the great age of modern American humour—the 1930s—and choosing an example of Robert Benchley in a predicament, Dorothy Parker in a peeve, Ogden Nash *in extremis*, and Ludwig Bemelmans in a baroque mood.

The most recent American humour to affect and not affront our British public comes mainly from television—but the theatre is a better and more permanent form of the same writing. For ten years now, the most popular successes of the

London stage have been musicals of the Rogers and Hammer-
stein calibre, and many of these were adapted and glorified
from comparatively humble books—*Guys and Dolls*, for instance, and the recent *Pajama Game*. It is here that the robust
and perennial American humour asserts itself.

But my earlier favourites have survived the years to an
astonishing degree, and I make no apology for including the
early work of the masters. They have a remarkable freshness
and resilience, even if they represent, in some instances, a hey-
day and a halcyon time, long before the H-bomb was born or
McCarthy held his court.

James Thurber

MUCH HAS been written about Thurber. Much more has been thought about him by those who instinctively understand him but cannot express themselves. I hesitate to add anything further, except to agree with those who believe the key to Thurber to be in his drawings. There is an undeniable note of triumph in E. B. White's postscript to *Is Sex Necessary?* It was White who, as we are told, saved Thurber for posterity, by collecting the 'restless scrawls' as they fell. It was the name of White which first recommended Thurber to Harold Ross of the *New Yorker*. Dorothy Parker, commenting on a Thurber collection, wrote:

> The artist has gone into the language. How often we say "He's a Thurber man" or "Look at that woman—she's a perfect Thurber", and, God help us and them, we are always understood. We need say no more about them.

Yes, the Thurber world has always been recognizable: the 'strong undercurrent of grief' which runs through the men, and the 'cold, flat look' which, in the master's phrase, 'one woman fetches another'. So it was ordained from the first. But much water has flowed since the day the Dam broke, and Thurber is becoming increasingly impelled to say a few disjointed things about his world, even to supply us with a few clues as to its meaning.

Summing up at fifty, he revealed his prime as 'a period which extended roughly from the year Lindbergh flew the Atlantic to the year coffee was rationed'. Comparing his drawings with his prose, he agrees that the former 'sometimes seem to have reached completion by some other route than the common one of intent', but claims that his stories were actually written and did not just materialize.

Now he has come full circle—though it isn't exactly a circle, for Thurber could never draw one properly. The reminiscences of childhood neighbours in *The Thurber Album* fill in some of the framework of the author's life and hard times in Columbus, Ohio. Nothing has changed in the furnishing of the Thurber room. The standard lamp is still there, the tasteless picture, the listless dog by the sofa, the sexes poised, watchful, merciless. But the whole atmosphere is just a little more cosy now, and I fear one day the Thurber man and Thurber woman are going to be tempted to pay each other a compliment. It would be a fearful price.

In offering some Thurber, then, I have chosen two classic pieces. 'The Night the Ghost Got In' mellows with the years, and 'Walter Mitty', now that the film is forgotten and we are quite sure about the ending, is just about the best short story of its kind written since—well, since Lindbergh flew the Atlantic. To choose from the gallery of sketches is well-nigh impossible, but those in *The Beast in Me* were some of the earliest to be picked off the floor, and decorate a masterful collaboration on a favourite subject. Even as early as 1929, Thurber and White were declaring that two factors in the modern world had been over-emphasized. One was aviation, the other sex. At least, since Lindbergh, we are supposed to have done something about aviation.

⬦

THE SECRET LIFE OF WALTER MITTY

"We're going through!" The Commander's voice was like thin ice breaking. He wore his full-dress uniform, with the heavily braided white cap pulled down rakishly over one cold grey eye. "We can't make it, sir. It's spoiling for a hurricane, if you ask me." "I'm not asking you, Lieutenant Berg," said the Commander. "Throw on the power lights! Rev her up to 8500! We're going through!" The pounding of the cylinders increased: ta-pocketa-pocketa-pocketa-pocketa-pocketa. The Commander stared at the ice forming on the pilot window. He walked over and twisted a row of complicated dials. "Switch on No 8 auxiliary!" he shouted. "Switch on No 8 auxiliary!" repeated Lieutenant Berg. "Full strength in No 3 turret!" shouted the Commander. "Full strength in No 3 turret!" The crew, bending to their various tasks in the huge, hurtling eight-engined Navy Hydroplane, looked at each other and grinned. "The Old Man'll get us through,"

16

they said to one another. "The Old Man ain't afraid of Hell!" . . .

"Not so fast! You're driving too fast!" said Mrs Mitty. "What are you driving so fast for?"

"Hmm?" said Walter Mitty. He looked at his wife, in the seat beside him, with shocked astonishment. She seemed grossly unfamiliar, like a strange woman who had yelled at him in a crowd. "You were up to fifty-five," she said. "You know I don't like to go more than forty. You were up to fifty-five." Walter Mitty drove on to Waterbury in silence, the roaring of the SN202 through the worst storm in twenty years of Navy flying fading in the remote, intimate airways of his mind. "You're tensed up again," said Mrs Mitty. "It's one of your days. I wish you'd let Dr Renshaw look you over."

Walter Mitty stopped the car in front of the building where his wife went to have her hair done. "Remember to get those overshoes while I'm having my hair done," she said. "I don't need overshoes," said Mitty. She put her mirror back into her bag. "We've been through all that," she said, getting out of the car. "You're not a young man any longer." He raced the engine a little. "Why don't you wear your gloves? Have you lost your gloves?" Walter Mitty reached in a pocket and brought out the gloves. He put them on, but after she had turned and gone into the building and he had driven on to a red light, he took them off again. "Pick it up, brother!" snapped a cop as the light changed, and Mitty hastily pulled on his gloves and lurched ahead. He drove around the streets aimlessly for a time, and then he drove past the hospital on his way to the parking lot.

. . . "It's the millionaire banker, Wellington McMillan," said the pretty nurse. "Yes?" said Walter Mitty, removing his gloves slowly. "Who has the case?" "Dr Renshaw and Dr Benbow, but there are two specialists here, Dr Remington from New York and Mr Pritchard-Mitford from London. He flew over." A door opened down a long, cool corridor and Dr Renshaw came out. He looked distraught and haggard. "Hello, Mitty," he said. "We're having the devil's own time with McMillan, the millionaire banker and close personal friend of Roosevelt. Obstreosis of the ductal tract. Tertiary. Wish you'd take a look at him." "Glad to," said Mitty.

In the operating-room there were whispered introductions:

"Dr Remington, Mr Mitty. Mr Pritchard-Mitford, Dr Mitty."
"I've read your book on streptothricosis," said Pritchard-Mitford, shaking hands. "A brilliant performance, sir."
"Thank you," said Walter Mitty. "Didn't know you were in the States, Mitty," grumbled Remington. "Coals to Newcastle, bringing Mitford and me up here for a tertiary." "You are very kind," said Mitty. A huge, complicated machine, connected to the operating table, with many tubes and wires, began at this moment to go pocketa-pocketa-pocketa. "The new anaesthetizer is giving way!" shouted an interne. "There is no one in the East who knows how to fix it!" "Quiet, man!" said Mitty, in a low, cool voice. He sprang to the machine, which was now going pocketa-pocketa-pocketa-queep-pocketa-queep. He began fingering delicately a row of glistening dials. "Give me a fountain pen!" he snapped. Someone handed him a fountain pen. He pulled a faulty piston out of the machine and inserted the pen in its place. "That will hold for ten minutes," he said. "Get on with the operation." A nurse hurried over and whispered to Renshaw, and Mitty saw the man turn pale. "Coreopsis has set in," said Renshaw nervously. "If you would take over, Mitty?" Mitty looked at him and at the craven figure of Benbow, who drank, and at the grave, uncertain faces of the two great specialists. "If you wish," he said. They slipped a white gown on him; he adjusted a mask and drew on thin gloves; nurses handed him a shining . . .

"Back it up, Mac! Look out for that Buick!" Walter Mitty jammed on the brakes. "Wrong lane, Mac," said the parking-lot attendant, looking at Mitty closely. "Gee, yeh," muttered Mitty. He began cautiously to back out of the lane marked 'Exit Only'. "Leave her sit there," said the attendant. "I'll put her away." Mitty got out of the car. "Hey, better leave the key." "Oh," said Mitty, handing the man the ignition key. The attendant vaulted into the car, backed it up with insolent skill, and put it where it belonged.

They're so damn cocky, thought Walter Mitty, walking along Main Street; they think they know everything. Once he had tried to take his chains off, outside New Milford, and he had got them wound around the axles. A man had had to come out in a wrecking car and unwind them, a young, grinning garage-man. Since then Mrs Mitty always made him drive to a garage to have the chains taken off. The next time, he thought, I'll wear my right arm in a sling; they won't grin at me then. I'll have my right arm in a sling and they'll see I couldn't possibly take the chains off myself. He kicked at the slush on the sidewalk. 'Overshoes,' he said to himself, and he began looking for a shoe store.

When he came out into the street again, with the overshoes in a box under his arm, Walter Mitty began to wonder what the other thing was his wife had told him to get. She had told him, twice, before they set out from their house for Waterbury. In a way he hated these weekly trips to town—he was always getting something wrong. Kleenex, he thought, Squibb's, razor blades? No. Toothpaste, toothbrush, bicarbonate, carborundum, initiative and referendum? He gave it up. But she would remember it. 'Where's the what's-its-name?' she would ask. 'Don't tell me you forgot the what's-its-name?' A newsboy went by shouting something about the Waterbury trial.

. . . "Perhaps this will refresh your memory." The District Attorney suddenly thrust a heavy automatic at the quiet figure on the witness stand. "Have you ever seen this before?" Walter Mitty took the gun and examined it expertly. "This is my Webley-Vickers 50.80," he said calmly. An excited buzz ran around the courtroom. The Judge rapped for order. "You are a crack shot with any sort of firearms, I believe?" said the District Attorney, insinuatingly. "Objection!" shouted Mitty's attorney. "We have shown that the defendant could not have fired the shot. We have shown that he wore his right arm in a sling on the night of the fourteenth of July." Walter Mitty raised his hand briefly and the bickering attorneys were stilled. "With any known make of gun," he said evenly, "I could have killed Gregory Fitzhurst at three hundred feet with my left hand." Pandemonium broke loose in the courtroom. A woman's scream rose above the bedlam and suddenly a lovely, dark-haired girl was in Walter Mitty's arms. The District Attorney struck at her savagely. Without rising from his chair, Mitty let the man have it on the point of the chin. "You miserable cur!" . . .

"Puppy biscuit," said Walter Mitty. He stopped walking and the buildings of Waterbury rose up out of the misty courtroom and surrounded him again. A woman who was passing laughed. "He said 'puppy biscuit'," she said to her companion. "That man said 'puppy biscuit' to himself." Walter Mitty hurried on. He went into an A. & P., not the first one he came to but a smaller one farther up the street. "I want some biscuit for small, young dogs," he said to the clerk. "Any special brand, sir?" The greatest pistol shot in the world thought for a moment. "It says 'Puppies Bark for it' on the box," said Walter Mitty.

His wife would be through at the hairdresser's in fifteen minutes, Mitty saw in looking at his watch, unless they had trouble drying it; sometimes they had trouble drying it. She didn't like to get to the hotel first; she would want him to be there waiting for her as usual. He found a big leather chair in the lobby, facing a window, and he put the overshoes and the puppy biscuit on the floor beside it. He picked up an old copy of *Liberty* and sank down into the chair. 'Can Germany Conquer the World Through the Air?' Walter Mitty looked at the pictures of bombing planes and of ruined streets.

. . . "The cannonading has got the wind up in young Raleigh, sir," said the sergeant. Captain Mitty looked up at him through tousled hair. "Get him to bed," he said wearily. "With the others. I'll fly alone." "But you can't, sir," said the sergeant anxiously. "It takes two men to handle that bomber and the Archies are pounding hell out of the air. Von Richtman's circus is between here and Saulier." "Somebody's got to get that ammunition dump," said Mitty. "I'm going over. Spot of brandy?" He poured a drink for the sergeant and one for himself. War thundered and whined around the dugout and battered at the door. There was a rending of wood and splinters flew through the room. "A bit of a near thing," said Captain Mitty carelessly. "The box barrage is closing in," said the sergeant. "We only live once, Sergeant," said Mitty, with his faint fleeting smile. "Or do we?" He poured another brandy and tossed it off. "I never see a man could hold his brandy like you, sir," said the sergeant. "Begging your pardon, sir." Captain Mitty stood up and strapped on his huge Webley-Vickers automatic. "It's forty kilometres through hell, sir," said the sergeant. Mitty finished one last brandy. "After all," he said softly, "what isn't?" The pounding of the cannon increased; there was the rat-tat-tatting of machine guns, and from somewhere came the menacing pocketa-pocketa-pocketa of the new flame-throwers. Walter Mitty walked to the door of the dugout humming 'Auprès de Ma Blonde'. He turned and waved to the sergeant. "Cheerio!" he said. . . .

Something struck his shoulder. "I've been looking all over this hotel for you," said Mrs Mitty. "Why do you have to hide in this old chair? How did you expect me to find you?" "Things close in," said Walter Mitty vaguely. "What?" Mrs Mitty said. "Did you get the what's-its-name? The puppy biscuit? What's in that box?" "Overshoes," said Mitty. "Couldn't you have put them on in the store?" "I was thinking," said Walter Mitty. "Does it ever occur to you that I am sometimes thinking?" She looked at him. "I'm going to take your temperature when I get home," she said.

They went out through the revolving doors that made a faintly derisive whistling sound when you pushed them. It was two blocks to the parking lot. At the drugstore on the corner she said, "Wait here for me. I forgot something. I won't be a minute." She was more than a minute. Walter Mitty lighted a cigarette. It began to rain, rain with sleet in it. He stood up against the wall of the drugstore, smoking. . . . He put his shoulders back and his heels together. "To hell with the handkerchief," said Walter Mitty scornfully. He took one last drag on his cigarette and snapped it away. Then, with that faint, fleeting smile playing about his lips, he faced the firing squad; erect and motionless, proud and disdainful, Walter Mitty the Undefeated, inscrutable to the last.

⟡

THE NIGHT THE GHOST GOT IN

The ghost that got into our house on the night of November 17th, 1915, raised such a hullabaloo of misunderstandings that I am sorry I didn't just let it keep on walking, and go to bed. Its advent caused my mother to throw a shoe through a window of the house next door and ended up with my grandfather shooting a patrolman. I am sorry, therefore, as I have said, that I ever paid any attention to the footsteps.

They began about a quarter past one o'clock in the morning, a rhythmic, quick-cadenced walking around the dining-room table. My mother was asleep in one room upstairs, my brother Herman in another; grandfather was in the attic, in the old walnut bed which, as you will remember, once fell on my father. I had just stepped out of the bathtub and was busily rubbing myself with a towel when I heard the steps. They were the steps of a man walking rapidly around the dining-room table downstairs. The light from the bathroom shone down the back steps, which dropped directly into the dining-room; I could see the faint shine of plates on the plate-rail; I couldn't see the table. The steps kept going round and round the table; at regular intervals a board creaked, when it was trod upon. I supposed at first that it was my father or my brother Roy, who had gone to Indianapolis but were expected home at any time. I suspected next that it was a burglar. It did not enter my mind until later that it was a ghost.

After the walking had gone on for perhaps three minutes, I tiptoed to Herman's room. "Psst!" I hissed, in the dark, shaking him. "Awp," he said, in the low, hopeless tone of a despondent beagle—he always half suspected that something would 'get him' in the night. I told him who I was. "There's something downstairs!" I said. He got up and followed me to the head of the back staircase. We listened together. There was no sound. The steps had ceased. Herman looked at me in some alarm: I had only the bath towel around my waist. He wanted to go back to bed, but I gripped his arm. "There's something down there," I said. Instantly the steps began again, circled the dining-room table like a man running, and started up the stairs towards us, heavily, two at a time. The light still shone palely down the stairs: we saw nothing coming; we only heard the steps. Herman rushed to his room and slammed the door. I slammed shut the door at the stairs top and held my knee against it. After a long minute, I slowly opened it again. There was nothing there. There was no sound. None of us ever heard the ghost again.

The slamming of the doors had aroused mother: she peered out of her room. "What on earth are you boys doing?" she demanded. Herman ventured out of his room. "Nothing," he said gruffly, but he was, in colour, a light green. "What was all that running around downstairs?" said mother. So she had heard the steps, too! We just looked at her. "Burglars!" she shouted, intuitively. I tried to quiet her by starting lightly downstairs.

"Come on, Herman," I said.

"I'll stay with mother," he said. "She's all excited."

I stepped back on to the landing.

"Don't either of you go a step," said mother. "We'll call the police." Since the phone was downstairs, I didn't see how

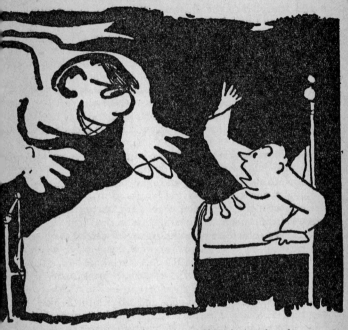

He always half suspected something would 'get him' in the night

we were going to call the police—nor did I want the police—but mother made one of her quick, incomparable decisions. She flung up a window of her bedroom which faced the bedroom windows of the house of a neighbour, picked up a shoe, and whammed it through a pane of glass across the narrow space that separated the two houses. Glass tinkled into the bedroom occupied by a retired engraver named Bodwell and

23

his wife. Bodwell had been for some years in rather a bad way and was subject to mild 'attacks'. Most everybody we knew or lived near had *some* kind of attacks.

It was now about two o'clock of a moonless night; clouds hung black and low. Bodwell was at the window in a minute, shouting, frothing a little, shaking his fist. "We'll sell the house and go back to Peoria," we could hear Mrs Bodwell saying. It was some time before mother 'got through' to Bodwell. "Burglars!" she shouted. "Burglars in the house!" Herman and I hadn't dared to tell her that it was not burglars but ghosts, for she was even more afraid of ghosts than of burglars. Bodwell at first thought that she meant there were burglars in his house, but finally he quieted down and called the police for us over an extension phone by his bed. After he had disappeared from the window, mother suddenly made as if to throw another shoe, not because there was further need of it, but, as she later explained, because the thrill of heaving a shoe through a window glass had enormously taken her fancy. I prevented her.

The police were on hand in a commendably short time: a Ford sedan full of them, two on motor-cycles, and a patrol wagon with about eight in it and a few reporters. They began banging at our front door. Flashlights shot streaks of gleam up and down the walls, across the yard, down the walk between our house and Bodwell's. "Open up!" cried a hoarse voice. "We're men from headquarters!" I wanted to go down and let them in, since there they were, but mother wouldn't hear of it. "You haven't a stitch on," she pointed out. "You'd catch your death." I wound the towel around me again. Finally the cops put their shoulders to our big heavy front door with its thick bevelled glass and broke it in: I could hear a rending of wood and a splash of glass on the floor of the hall. Their lights played all over the living-room and criss-crossed nervously in the dining-room, stabbed into hallways, shot up the front stairs, and finally up the back. They caught me standing in my towel at the top. A heavy policeman bounded up the steps. "Who are you?" he demanded. "I live here," I said. "Well, whattsa matta, ya hot?" he asked. It was, as a matter of fact, cold; I went to my room and pulled on some trousers. On my way out, a cop stuck a gun into my ribs. "Whatta you doin' here?" he demanded. "I live here," I said.

The officer in charge reported to mother. "No sign of no-body, lady," he said. "Musta got away—whatt'd he look like?" "There were two or three of them," mother said, "whooping and carrying on and slamming doors." "Funny," said the cop. "All ya windows and doors was locked on the inside tight as a tick."

Downstairs, we could hear the tramping of the other police. Police were all over the place; doors were yanked open, drawers were yanked open, windows were shot up and pulled

Police were all over the place

down, furniture fell with dull thumps. A half-dozen police-men emerged out of the darkness of the front hallway up-stairs. They began to ransack the floor: pulled beds away from walls, tore clothes off hooks in the closets, pulled suitcases and boxes off shelves. One of them found an old zither that Roy had won in a pool tournament. "Looky here, Joe," he said, strumming it with a big paw. The cop named Joe took it and turned it over. "What is it?" he asked me. "It's an old zither our guinea pig used to sleep on," I said. It was true that a pet guinea pig we once had would never sleep anywhere except on the zither, but I should never have said so. Joe and the other cop looked at me a long time. They put the zither back on a shelf.

"No sign o' nothing," said the cop who had first spoken to mother. "This guy," he explained to the others, jerking a thumb at me, "was nekked. The lady seems historical." They all nodded, but said nothing; just looked at me. In the small silence we all heard a creaking in the attic. Grandfather was turning over in bed. "What's 'at?" snapped Joe. Five or six cops sprang for the attic door before I could intervene or explain. I realized that it would be bad if they burst in on grandfather unannounced, or even announced. He was going through a phase in which he believed that General Meade's men, under steady hammering by Stonewall Jackson, were beginning to retreat and even desert.

When I got to the attic, things were pretty confused. Grandfather had evidently jumped to the conclusion that the police were deserters from Meade's army, trying to hide away in his attic. He bounded out of bed wearing a long flannel nightgown over long woollen underwear, a nightcap, and a leather jacket around his chest. The cops must have realized at once that the indignant white-haired old man belonged in the house, but they had no chance to say so. "Back, ye cowardly dogs!" roared grandfather. "Back t'the lines, ye goddam lily-livered cattle!" With that, he fetched the officer who found the zither a flat-handed smack alongside his head that sent him sprawling. The others beat a retreat, but not fast enough; grandfather grabbed zither's gun from its holster and let fly. The report seemed to crack the rafters; smoke filled the attic. A cop cursed and shot his hand to his shoulder. Somehow, we all finally got downstairs again and locked the door against the old gentleman. He fired once or twice more in the darkness and then went back to bed. "That was grandfather," I explained to Joe, out of breath. "He thinks you're deserters." "I'll say he does," said Joe.

The cops were reluctant to leave without getting their hands on somebody besides grandfather; the night had been distinctly a defeat for them. Furthermore, they obviously didn't like the 'layout'; something looked—and I can see their viewpoint—phony. They began to poke into things again. A reporter, a thin-faced, wispy man, came up to me. I had put on one of mother's blouses, not being able to find anything else.

26

The reporter looked at me with mingled suspicion and interest. "Just what the hell is the real lowdown here, Bud?" he asked. I decided to be frank with him. "We had ghosts," I said. He gazed at me a long time as if I were a slot machine into which he had, without results, dropped a nickel. Then he walked away. The cops followed him, the one grandfather shot holding his now-bandaged arm, cursing and blaspheming. "I'm gonna get my gun back from that old bird," said the zither-cop. "Yeh," said Joe. "You—and who else?" I told them I would bring it to the station house the next day.

"What was the matter with that one policeman?" mother asked, after they had gone. "Grandfather shot him," I said. "What for?" she demanded. I told her he was a deserter. "Of all things!" said mother. "He was such a nice-looking young man."

Grandfather was fresh as a daisy and full of jokes at breakfast next morning. We thought at first he had forgotten all about what had happened, but he hadn't. Over his third cup of coffee, he glared at Herman and me. "What was the idee of all them cops tarryhootin' round the house last night?" he demanded. He had us there.

⬦

THE LADY ON THE BOOKCASE

One day twelve years ago an outraged cartoonist, four of whose drawings had been rejected in a clump by the *New Yorker*, stormed into the office of Harold Ross, editor of the magazine. "Why is it," demanded the cartoonist, "that you reject my work and publish drawings by a fifth-rate artist like Thurber?" Ross came quickly to my defence like the true friend and devoted employer he is. "You mean third-rate," he said quietly, but there was a warning glint in his steady grey eyes that caused the discomfited cartoonist to beat a hasty retreat.

With the exception of Ross, the interest of editors in what I draw has been rather more journalistic than critical. They want to know if it is true that I draw by moonlight, or under water, and when I say no, they lose interest until they hear the

With you I have known peace, Lida, and now you say you're
going crazy

Home

rumour that I found the drawings in an old trunk or that I do the captions while my nephew makes the sketches.

The other day I was shoving some of my originals around on the floor (I do not draw on the floor; I was just shoving the originals around) and they fell, or perhaps I pushed them, into five separate and indistinct categories. I have never wanted to write about my drawings, and I still don't want to, but it occurred to me that it might be a good idea to do it now, when everybody is busy with something else, and get it over quietly.

Category No 1, then, which may be called the Unconscious or Stream of Nervousness category, is represented by 'With you I have known peace, Lida, and now you say you're going crazy' and the drawing entitled, with simple dignity, 'Home'. These drawings were done while the artist was thinking of something else (or so he has been assured by experts), and hence his hand was guided by the Unconscious, which, in turn, was more or less influenced by the Subconscious.

Students of Jung have instructed me that Lida and the House-woman are representations of the anima, the female essence or directive which floats around in the ageless universal Subconscious of Man like a tadpole in a cistern. Less intellectual critics insist that the two ladies are actual persons I have consciously known. Between these two schools of thought lies a discouragingly large space of time extending roughly from 1,000,000 BC to the middle Nineteen Thirties.

Whenever I try to trace the true identity of the House-woman, I get to thinking of Mr Jones. He appeared in my office one day twelve years ago, said he was Mr Jones, and asked me to lend him 'Home' for reproduction in an art magazine. I never saw the drawing again. Tall, well-dressed, kind of sad-looking chap, and as well spoken a gentleman as you would want to meet.

Category No 2 brings us to Freud and another one of those discouragingly large spaces—namely, the space between the Concept of the Purely Accidental and the Theory of Haphazard Determination. Whether chance is capricious or we are all prisoners of pattern is too long and cloudy a subject to go into here. I shall consider each of the drawings in Category No 2, explaining what happened and leaving the definition of the forces involved up to you. The seal on top of the bed, then ('All right, have it your way—you heard a seal bark'),

All right, have it your way—you heard a seal bark

That's my first wife up there, and this is the present *Mrs Harris*

started out to be a seal on a rock. The rock, in the process of being drawn, began to look like the head of a bed, so I made a bed out of it, put a man and wife in the bed, and stumbled on to the caption as easily and unexpectedly as the seal had stumbled into the bedroom.

The woman on top of the bookcase ('That's my first wife up there, and this is the *present* Mrs Harris') was originally designed to be a woman crouched on the top step of a staircase,

*For the last time, you and your horsie get away from me
and stay away!*

but since the tricks and conventions of perspective and planes sometimes fail me, the staircase assumed the shape of a bookcase and was finished as such, to the surprise and embarrassment of the first Mrs Harris, the present Mrs Harris, the lady visitor, Mr Harris and me. Before the *New Yorker* would print the drawing they phoned me long distance to inquire whether the first Mrs Harris was alive or dead or stuffed. I replied that my taxidermist had advised me that you cannot stuff a woman, and that my physician had informed me that a dead lady cannot support herself on all fours. This meant, I said, that the first Mrs Harris was unquestionably alive.

The man riding on the other man's shoulders in the bar ('For the last time, you and your horsie get away from me and stay away!') was intended to be standing alongside the irate speaker, but I started his head up too high and made it too small, so that he would have been nine feet tall if I had completed his body that way. It was but the work of thirty-two seconds to put him on another man's shoulders. As simple or, if you like, as complicated as that. The psychological factors which may be present here are, as I have indicated, elaborate

The father belonged to some people who were driving through
in a Packard

and confused. Personally I like Dr Claude Thornway's theory of the Deliberate Accident or Conditioned Mistake.

Category No 3 is perhaps a variant of Category No 2; indeed, they may even be identical. The dogs in 'The father belonged to some people who were driving through in a Packard' were drawn as a captionless spot, and the interior with figures just sort of grew up around them. The hippopotamus in 'What have you done with Dr Millmoss?' was drawn to amuse my small daughter. Something about the creature's expression when he was completed convinced me that he had recently eaten a man. I added the hat and pipe and Mrs Mill-

What have you done with Dr Millmoss?

moss, and the caption followed easily enough. Incidentally, my daughter, who was two years old at the time, identified the beast immediately. "That's a hippotomanus," she said. The *New Yorker* was not so smart. They described the drawing for

Touché!

their files as follows: 'Woman with strange animal.' The *New Yorker* was nine years old at the time.

Category No 4 is represented by perhaps the best known of some fifteen drawings belonging to this special grouping, which may be called the Contributed Idea Category. This drawing ('Touché!') was originally done for the *New Yorker* by Carl Rose, caption and all. Mr Rose is a realistic artist, and his gory scene distressed the editors, who hate violence. They asked Rose if he would let me have the idea, since there is obviously no blood to speak of in the people I draw. Rose graciously consented. No one who looks at 'Touché!' believes that the man whose head is in the air is really dead. His opponent will hand it back to him with profuse apologies, and the discommoded fencer will replace it on his shoulders and say, "No harm done, forget it." Thus the old controversy as to whether death can be made funny is left just where it was before Carl Rose came along with his wonderful idea.

Category No 5, our final one, can be called, believe it or not, the Intentional or Thought-up Category. The idea for each of these two drawings just came to me and I sat down and made a sketch to fit the prepared caption. Perhaps, in the case of 'Well, I'm disenchanted, too. We're all disenchanted,'

Well, I'm disenchanted, too. We're all disenchanted

another one of those Outside Forces played a part. That is, I may have overheard a husband say to his wife, on the street or at a party, "I'm disenchanted." I do not think this is true, however, in the case of the rabbit-headed doctor and his woman patient. I believe that scene and its caption came to me one night in bed. I *may* have got the idea in a doctor's office or a rabbit hutch, but I don't think so.

You said a moment ago that everybody you look at seems to be a rabbit. Now just what do you mean by that, Mrs Sprague?

If you want to, you can cut these drawings out and push them around on the floor, making your own categories or applying your own psychological theories; or you can even invent some fresh rumours. I should think it would be more fun, though, to take a nap, or baste a roast, or run around the reservoir in Central Park.

Don Marquis

IN THE winter of 1931, review copies went out from a London publisher of a book set entirely in what printers call 'lower case'. The complete absence of capitals in *archy and mehitabel*, with the preposterous explanation offered by Don Marquis, the author, made an immediate appeal. After all, 1931 was a mad, before-the-deluge year. And so archy fulfilled his promise and became famous.

> i will write you a series of poems showing how
>   things look
> to a cockroach

> don t you ever eat any sandwiches in your office
> i haven t had a crumb of bread for i don t
>   know how long
> or a piece of ham or anything but apple parings
> and paste leave a piece of paper in your machine
> every night you can call me archy

The laconic poems about the cockroach and the cat mehitabel have remained with us for two decades, though the cult of 'lower case' died early. I have always cherished 'cheerio my deario' as one of the great songs, and if you think archy's poems are mere echoes and lunacy, analyse the literary criticism of 'pete the parrot and shakespeare'. After reading it, one is not surprised to find that Don Marquis nursed a secret wish to be known for his serious writing as well—and that included novels set in New York and Paris, Negro sketches, satires in the manner of Mark Twain, Elizabethan comedies, a play about Christ and a dramatic version of the Tristan and Iseult legend.

But he was beaten by his own cockroach, and was, I hope, content at the result. I know an American living in Le Havre whose dog, he claims, can type, capitals and all. When will it end, this desire of Americans to involve animals in their human contrivances?

&

cheerio my deario

well boss i met
mehitabel the cat
trying to dig a
frozen lamb chop
out of a snow
drift the other day

a heluva comedown
that is for me archy
she says a few
brief centuries
ago one of old
king
tut
ankh
amen s favorite
queens and today
the village scavenger
but wotthehell
archy wotthehell
it s cheerio
my deario that
pulls a lady through

see here mehitabel
i said i thought
you told me that
it was cleopatra
you used to be
before you
transmigrated into
the carcase of a cat
where do you get
this tut

ankh
amen stuff
question mark

i was several
ladies my little
insect says she
being cleopatra was
only an incident
in my career
and i was always getting
the rough end of it
always being
misunderstood by some
strait laced
prune faced bunch
of prissy mouthed
sisters of uncharity
the things that
have been said
about me archy
exclamation point

and all simply
because i was a
live dame
the palaces i have
been kicked out of
in my time
exclamation point
but wotthehell
little archy wot
thehell
it s cheerio
my deario
that pulls a
lady through
exclamation point

framed archy always
framed that is the
story of all my lives

no chance for a dame
with the anvil chorus
if she shows a little
motion it seems to
me only yesterday
that the luxor local
number one of
the ladies axe
association got me in
dutch with king tut and
he slipped me the
sarcophagus always my
luck yesterday an empress
and today too
emaciated to interest
a vivisectionist but
toujours gai archy
toujours gai and always
a lady in spite of hell
and transmigration
once a queen
always a queen
archy
period

one of her
feet was frozen
but on the other three
she began to caper and
dance singing it s
cheerio my deario
that pulls a lady
through her morals may
have been mislaid somewhere
in the centuries boss but
i admire her spirit

                    archy

pete the parrot and shakespeare

i got acquainted with
a parrot named pete recently
who is an interesting bird
pete says he used
to belong to the fellow
that ran the mermaid tavern
in london then i said
you must have known
shakespeare know him said pete
poor mutt i knew him well
he called me pete and i called him
bill but why do you say poor mutt
well said pete bill was a
disappointed man and was always
boring his friends about what
he might have been and done
if he only had a fair break
two or three pints of sack
and sherris and the tears
would trickle down into his
beard and his beard would get
soppy and wilt his collar
i remember one night when
bill and ben jonson and
frankie beaumont
were sopping it up

here i am ben says bill
nothing but a lousy playwright
and with anything like luck
in the breaks i might have been
a fairly decent sonnet writer
i might have been a poet
if i had kept away from the theatre
yes says ben i ve often
thought of that bill
but one consolation is

you are making pretty good money
out of the theatre

money money says bill what the hell
is money what i want is to be
a poet not a business man
these damned cheap shows
i turn out to keep the
theatre running break my heart
slap stick comedies and
blood and thunder tragedies
and melodramas say i wonder
if that boy heard you order
another bottle frankie
the only compensation is that i get
a chance now and then
to stick in a little poetry
when nobody is looking
but hells bells that isn t
what i want to do
i want to write sonnets and
songs and spenserian stanzas
and i might have done it too
if i hadn t got
into this frightful show game
business business business
grind grind grind
what a life for a man
that might have been a poet

well says frankie beaumont
why don t you cut it bill
i can t says bill
i need the money i ve got
a family to support down in
the country well says frankie
anyhow you write pretty good
plays bill any mutt can write
plays for this london public
says bill if he puts enough
murder in them what they want

is kings talking like kings
never had sense enough to talk
and stabbings and stranglings
and fat men making love
and clowns basting each
other with clubs and cheap puns
and off colour allusions to all
the smut of the day oh i know
what the low brows want
and i give it to them

well says ben jonson
don t blubber into the drink
brace up like a man
and quit the rotten business
i can t i can t says bill
i ve been at it too long i ve got to
the place now where i can t
write anything else
but this cheap stuff
i m ashamed to look an honest
young sonneteer in the face
I live a hell of a life i do
the manager hands me some mouldy old
manuscript and says
bill here s a plot for you
this is the third of the month
by the tenth i want a good
script out of this that we
can start rehearsals on
not too big a cast
and not too much of your
damned poetry either
you know your old
familiar line of hokum
they eat up that falstaff stuff
of yours bring him in again
and give them a good ghost
or two and remember we gotta
have something dick burbage can get
his teeth into and be sure

and stick in a speech
somewhere the queen will take
for a personal compliment and if
you get in a line or two somewhere
about the honest english yeoman
it s always good stuff
and it s a pretty good stunt
bill to have a heavy villain
a moor or a dago or a jew
or something like that and say
i want another
comic welshman in this
but i don t need to tell
you bill you know this game
just some of your ordinary
hokum and maybe you could
kill a little kid or two a prince
or something they like
a little pathos along with
the dirt now you better see burbage
tonight and see what he wants
in that part oh says bill
to think I am
debasing my talents with junk
like that oh god what i wanted
was to be a poet
and write sonnet serials
like a gentleman should

well says i pete
bill s plays are highly
esteemed to this day
is that so says pete
poor mutt little he would
care what poor bill wanted
was to be a poet

archy

A REALLY 'DUMB' woman is surely one who is not even thinking the things she is *not* saying. The dumb blondes of American fiction, be they created in sketch by Peter Arno, in print by Miss Loos or on film by Marilyn Monroe, are endowed with a sort of peasant cunning which can only endure a limited amount of tuition. When Peter Arno's male character points to his blonde companion and says to the bartender, "Fill her up," he is indicating someone really dumb. But the blonde in *Born Yesterday* yelling at the tycoon "You're not couth!" is already caught in Pygmalion's fatal toils of reasoning.

The perfect Blonde, the original Girl the Gentlemen first Preferred, was Mr Eisman's friend. "He is quite anxious," she wrote in her diary, "for a girl to improve her mind and his greatest interest in me is because I always want to improve my mind and not waste any time." But the next day, Mr Eisman's birthday diamond was much too small, "a little thing you could hardly see".

There is no longer any sense of shock or naughtiness in the diary of the professional lady, but reading this first chapter of *Gentlemen Prefer Blondes*, it is surprising to find how fresh Miss Loos's frail looks today, like a film actress making a triumphant comeback on television.

⬥

GENTLEMEN PREFER BLONDES

March 16th: A gentleman friend and I were dining at the Ritz last evening and he said that if I took a pencil and a paper and put down all of my thoughts it would make a book. This almost made me smile, as what it would really make would be a whole row of encyclopediacs. I mean I seem to be thinking practically all of the time. I mean it is my favourite recreation and sometimes I sit for hours and do not seem to do anything else but think. So this gentleman said a girl with brains ought to do something else with them besides think. And he said he ought to know brains when he sees them, because he is in the senate and he spends quite a great deal of time in Washington, d.c., and when he comes into contact with brains he always notices it. So it might have all blown over but this morning he sent me a book. And so when my maid brought it to me, I said to her, "Well, Lulu, here is another book and we have not read half the ones we have got yet." But when I opened it and saw that it was all a blank I remembered what my gentleman acquaintance said, and so then I realized that it was a diary. So here I am writing a book instead of reading one.

But now it is the 16th March and of course it is too late to begin with January, but it does not matter as my gentleman friend, Mr Eisman, was in town practically all of January and February, and when he is in town one day seems to be practically the same as the next day.

I mean Mr Eisman is in the wholesale button profession in Chicago and he is the gentleman who is known practically all over Chicago as Gus Eisman the Button King. And he is the gentleman who is interested in educating me, so of course he is always coming down to New York to see how my brains have improved since the last time. But when Mr Eisman is in New York we always seem to do the same thing and if I wrote down one day in my diary, all I would have to do would be to put quotation marks for all other days. I mean we always seem to have dinner at the Colony and see a show and go to the Trocadero and then Mr Eisman shows me to my apartment. So of course when a gentleman is interested in educating a girl, he likes to stay and talk about the topics of the day until quite late, so I am quite fatigued the next day and I do not really get up until it is time to dress for dinner at the Colony.

It would be strange if I turn out to be an authoress. I mean at my home near Little Rock, Arkansas, my family all wanted me to do something about my music. Because all of my friends said I had talent and they all kept after me and kept after me about practising. But some way I never seemed to care so much about practising. I mean I simply could not sit for hours and hours at a time practising just for the sake of a career. So one day I got quite temperamental and threw the old mandolin clear across the room and I have really never touched it since. But writing is different because you do not have to learn or practise and it is more temperamental because practising seems to take all the temperament out of me. So now I really almost have to smile because I have just noticed that I have written clear across two pages on to March 18th, so this will do for today and tomorrow. And it just shows how temperamental I am when I get started.

March 19th: Well last evening Dorothy called up and Dorothy said she has met a gentleman who gave himself an introduction to her in the lobby of the Ritz. So then they went to luncheon and tea and dinner and then they went to a show and then they went to the Trocadero. So Dorothy said his name was Lord Cooksleigh but what she really calls him is Coocoo. So Dorothy said why don't you and I and Coocoo go to the Follies tonight and bring Gus along if he is in town? So then Dorothy and I had quite a little quarrel because every time that Dorothy mentions the subject of Mr Eisman she calls Mr Eisman by his first name, and she does not seem to realize that when a gentleman who is as important as Mr Eisman spends quite a lot of money educating a girl, it really does not show reverence to call a gentleman by his first name. I mean I never even think of calling Mr Eisman by his first name, but if I want to call him anything at all, I call him 'Daddy' and I do not even call him 'Daddy' if a place seems to be public. So I told Dorothy that Mr Eisman would not be in town until day after tomorrow. So then Dorothy and Coocoo came up and we went to the Follies.

So this morning Coocoo called up and he wanted me to luncheon at the Ritz. I mean these foreigners really have quite a nerve. Just because Coocoo is an Englishman and a Lord he thinks a girl can waste hours on him just for a luncheon at the Ritz, when all he does is talk about some exposition he went on to a place called Tibet and after talking for hours I found out that all they were was a lot of Chinamen. So I will be quite glad to see Mr Eisman when he gets in. Because he always has something quite interesting to talk about, as for instants the last time he was here he presented me with quite a beautiful emerald bracelet. So next week is my birthday and he always has some delightful surprise on holidays.

I did intend to luncheon at the Ritz with Dorothy today and of course Coocoo had to spoil it, as I told him that I could not luncheon with him today, because my brother was in town on business and had the mumps, so I really could not leave him alone. Because of course if I went to the Ritz now I would bump into Coocoo. But I sometimes almost have to smile at my own imagination, because of course I have not got any brother and I have not even thought of the mumps for years. I mean it is no wonder that I can write.

So the reason I thought I would take luncheon at the Ritz was because Mr Chaplin is at the Ritz and I always like to renew old acquaintances, because I met Mr Chaplin once when we were both working on the same lot in Hollywood and I am sure he would remember me. Gentlemen always seem to remember blondes. I mean the only career I would like to be besides an authoress is a cinema star and I was doing quite well in the cinema when Mr Eisman made me give it all up. Because of course when a gentleman takes such a friendly interest in educating a girl as Mr Eisman does, you like to show that you appreciate it, and he is against a girl being in the cinema because his mother is authrodox.

March 20th: Mr Eisman gets in tomorrow to be here in time for my birthday. So I thought it would really be delightful to have at least one good time before Mr Eisman got in, so last evening I had some literary gentlemen in to spend the evening because Mr Eisman always likes me to have literary people in and out of the apartment. I mean he is quite anxious for a girl to improve her mind and his greatest interest in me is because I always seem to want to improve my mind and not waste any time. And Mr Eisman likes me to have what the French people call a 'salon' which means that people all get together in the evening and improve their minds. So I invited all of the brainy gentlemen I could think up. So I thought up a gentleman who is the professor of all of the economics up at Columbia College, and the editor who is the famous editor of the *New York Transcript* and another gentleman who is a famous playright who writes very, very famous plays that are all about Life. I mean anybody would recognize his name but it always seems to slip my memory because all of we real friends of his only call him Sam. So Sam asked if he could bring a gentleman

47

who writes novels from England, so I said yes, so he brought him. And then we all got together and I called up Gloria and Dorothy and the gentlemen brought their own liquor. So of course the place was a wreck this morning and Lulu and I worked like the proverbial dogs to get it cleaned up, but Heaven knows how long it will take to get the chandelier fixed.

March 22nd: Well my birthday has come and gone but it really was quite depressing. I mean it seems to me a gentleman who has a friendly interest in educating a girl like Gus Eisman, would want her to have the biggest square cut diamond in New York. I mean I must say I was quite disappointed when he came to the apartment with a little thing you could hardly see. So I told him I thought it was quite cute, but I had quite a headache and I had better stay in a dark room all day and I told him I would see him the next day, perhaps. Because even Lulu thought it was quite small and she said, if she was I, she really would do something definite and she said she always believed in the old addage, 'Leave them while you're looking good.' But he came in at dinner time with really a very very beautiful bracelet of square cut diamonds so I was quite cheered up. So then we had dinner at the Colony and we went to a show and supper at the Trocadero as usual whenever he is in town. But I will give him credit that he realized how small it was. I mean he kept talking about how bad business was the button profession was full of bolshevicks who make nothing but trouble. Because Mr Eisman feels that the country is really on the verge of the bolshevicks and I become quite worried. I mean if the bolshevicks do get in, there is only one gentleman who could handle them and that is Mr D. W. Griffith. Because I will never forget when Mr Griffith was directing Intolerance. I mean it was my last cinema just before Mr Eisman made me give up my career and I was playing one of the girls that fainted at the battle when all of the gentlemen fell off the tower. And when I saw how Mr Griffith handled all of those mobs in Intolerance I realized that he could do anything, and I really think that the government of America ought to tell Mr Griffith to get all ready if the bolshevicks start to do it.

Well I forgot to mention that the English gentleman who

writes novels seems to have taken quite an interest in me, as soon as he found out that I was literary. I mean he has called up every day and I went to tea twice with him. So he has sent me a whole complete set of books for my birthday by a gentleman called Mr Conrad. They all seem to be about ocean travel although I have not had time to more than glance through them. I have always liked novels about ocean travel ever since I posed for Mr Christie for the front cover of a novel about ocean travel by McGrath because I always say that a girl never really looks as well as she does on board a steamship, or even a yacht.

So the English gentleman's name is Mr Gerald Lamson as those who have read his novels would know. And he also sent me some of his own novels and they all seem to be about middle age English gentlemen who live in the country over in London and seem to ride bicycles, which seems quite different from America, except at Palm Beach. So I told Mr Lamson how I write down all of my thoughts and he said he knew I had something to me from the first minute he saw me and when we become better acquainted I am going to let him read my diary. I mean I even told Mr Eisman about him and he is quite pleased. Because of course Mr Lamson is quite famous and it seems Mr Eisman has read all of his novels going to and fro on the trains and Mr Eisman is always anxious to meet famous people and take them to the Ritz to dinner on Saturday night. But of course I did not tell Mr Eisman that I am really getting quite a little crush on Mr Lamson, which I really believe I am, but Mr Eisman thinks my interest in him is more literary.

March 30th: At last Mr Eisman has left on the 20th Century and I must say I am quite fatigued and a little rest will be quite welcome. I mean I do not mind staying out late every night if I dance, but Mr Eisman is really not such a good dancer so most of the time we just sit and drink some champagne or have a bite to eat and of course I do not dance with anyone else when I am out with Mr Eisman. But Mr Eisman and Gerry, as Mr Lamson wants me to call him, became quite good friends and we had several evenings, all three together. So now that Mr Eisman is out of town at last, Gerry and I are going out together this evening and Gerry said not to dress

49

up, because Gerry seems to like me more for my soul. So I really had to tell Gerry that if all the gentlemen were like he seems to be, Madame Frances' whole dress making establishment would have to go out of business. But Gerry does not like a girl to be nothing else but a doll, but he likes her to bring in her husband's slippers every evening and make him forget what he has gone through.

But before Mr Eisman went to Chicago he told me that he is going to Paris this summer on professional business and I think he intends to present me with a trip to Paris as he says there is nothing so educational as travelling. I mean it did worlds of good to Dorothy when she went abroad last spring and I never get tired of hearing her telling how the merry-go-rounds in Paris have pigs instead of horses. But I really do not know whether to be thrilled or not because, of course, if I go to Paris I will have to leave Gerry and both Gerry and I have made up our minds not to be separated from one another from now on.

March 31st: Last night Gerry and I had dinner at quite a quaint place where we had roast beef and baked potato. I mean he always wants me to have food which is what he calls 'Nourishing', which most gentlemen never seem to think about. So then we took a hansom cab and drove for hours around the park because Gerry said the air would be good for me. It is really very sweet to have someone think of all those things that gentlemen hardly ever seem to think about. So then we talked quite a lot. I mean Gerry knows how to draw a girl out and I told him things that I really would not even put in my diary. So when he heard all about my life he became quite depressed and we both had tears in our eyes. Because he said he never dreamed a girl could go through so much as I, and come out so sweet and not made bitter by it all. I mean Gerry thinks that most gentlemen are brutes and hardly ever think about a girl's soul.

So it seems that Gerry has had quite a lot of trouble himself and he can not even get married on account of his wife. He and she have never been in love with each other but she was a suffragette and asked him to marry her, so what could he do? So we rode all around the park until quite late talking and philosophizing quite a lot and I finally told him that I thought, after all, that bird life was the highest form of civilazation. So Gerry calls me his little thinker and I really would not be surprised if all of my thoughts will give him quite a few ideas for his novels. Because Gerry says he has never seen a girl of my personal appearance with so many brains. And he had almost given up looking for his ideal when our paths seemed to cross each other and I told him I really thought a thing like that was nearly always the result of fate.

So Gerry says that I remind him quite a lot of Helen of Troy, who was of Greek extraction. But the only Greek I know is a Greek gentleman by the name of Mr Georgopolis who is really quite wealthy and he is what Dorothy and I call a 'Shopper' because you can always call him up at any hour and ask him to go shopping and he is always quite delighted, which very few gentlemen seem to be. And he never seems to care how much anything costs. I mean Mr Georgopolis is also quite cultured, as I know quite a few gentlemen who can speak to a waiter in French but Mr Georgopolis can also speak to a waiter in Greek which very few gentlemen seem to be able to do.

April 1st: I am taking special pains with my diary from now on as I am really writing it for Gerry. I mean he and I are going to read it together some evening in front of the fireplace. But Gerry leaves this evening for Boston as he has to lecture about all of his works at Boston, but he will rush right back as soon as possible. So I am going to spend all of my time improving myself while he is gone. And this afternoon we are both going to a museum on 5th Avenue, because Gerry wants to show me a very very beautiful cup made by an antique jeweler called Mr Cellini and he wants me to read Mr Cellini's life which is a very very fine book and not dull while he is in Boston.

So the famous playright friend of mine who is called Sam called up this morning and he wanted me to go to a literary party tonight that he and some other literary gentlemen are giving to Florence Mills in Harlem but Gerry does not want me to go with Sam as Sam always insists on telling riskay stories. But personally I am quite broad minded and I always say that I do not mind a riskay story as long as it is really funny. I mean I have a great sense of humor. But Gerry says

Sam does not always select and choose his stories and he just as soon I did not go out with him. So I am going to stay home and read the book by Mr Cellini instead, because, after all, the only thing I am really interested in, is improving my mind. So I am going to do nothing else but improve my mind while Gerry is in Boston. I mean I just received a cable from Willie Gwynn who arrives from Europe tomorrow, but I am not even going to bother to see him. He is a sweet boy but he never gets anywhere and I am not going to waste my time on such as him, after meeting a gentleman like Gerry.

April 2nd: I seem to be quite depressed this morning as I always am when there is nothing to put my mind to. Because I decided not to read the book by Mr Cellini. I mean it was quite amuseing in spots because it was really quite riskay but the spots were not so close together and I never seem to like to always be hunting clear through a book for the spots I am looking for, especially when there are really not so many spots that seem to be so amuseing after all. So I did not waste my time on it but this morning I told Lulu to let all of the house work go and spend the day reading a book entitled 'Lord Jim' and then tell me all about it, so that I would improve my mind while Gerry is away. But when I got her the book I nearly made a mistake and gave her a book by the title of 'The Nigger of the Narcissus' which really would have hurt her feelings. I mean I do not know why authors cannot say 'Negro' instead of 'Nigger' as they have their feelings just the same as we have.

Well I have just got a telegram from Gerry that he will not be back until tomorrow and also some orchids from Willie Gwynn, so I may as well go to the theatre with Willie tonight to keep from getting depressed, as he really is a sweet boy after all. I mean he never really does anything obnoxious. And it is quite depressing to stay at home and do nothing but read, unless you really have a book that is worth bothering about.

April 3rd: I was really so depressed this morning that I was even glad to get a letter from Mr Eisman. Because last night Willie Gwynn came to take me to the Follies, but he was so intoxicated that I had to telephone his club to send around a taxi to take him home. So that left me alone with Lulu at nine o'clock with nothing to do, so I put in a telephone call for Boston to talk to Gerry but it never went through. So Lulu tried to teach me how to play mah jong, but I really could not keep my mind on it because I was so depressed. So today I think I had better go over to Madame Frances and order some new evening gowns to cheer me up.

Well Lulu has just brought me a telegram from Gerry that he will be in this afternoon, but I must not meet him at the station on account of all of the reporters who always meet him at the station wherever he comes from. But he says he will come right up to see me as he has something to talk about.

April 4th: What an evening we had last evening. I mean it seems that Gerry is madly in love with me. Because all of the time he was in Boston lecturing to the women's clubs he said, as he looked over the faces of all those club women in Boston, he never realized I was so beautiful. And he said that there was only one in all the world and that was me. But it seems that Gerry thinks that Mr Eisman is terrible and that no good can come of our friendship. I mean I was quite surprised, as they both seemed to get along quite well together, but it seems that Gerry never wants me to see Mr Eisman again. And he wants me to give up everything and study French and he will get a divorce and we will be married. Because Gerry does not seem to like the kind of life all of us lead in New York and he wants me to go home to papa in Arkansas and he will send me books to read so that I will not get lonesome there. And he gave me his uncle's Masonic ring, which came down from the time of Solomon and which he never even lets his wife wear, for our engagement ring, and this afternoon a lady friend of his is going to bring me a new system she thought up of how to learn French. But some way I still seem to be depressed. I mean I could not sleep all night thinking of the terrible things Gerry said about New York and about Mr Eisman. Of course I can understand Gerry being jealous of any gentleman friend of mine and of course I never really thought that Mr Eisman was Rudolph Valentino, but Gerry said it made him cringe to think of a sweet girl like I having friendship with Mr Eisman.

So it really made me feel quite depressed. I mean Gerry likes to talk quite a lot and I always think a lot of talk is depressing and worries your brains with things you never even think of when you are busy. But so long as Gerry does not mind me going out with other gentlemen when they have something to give you mentally, I am going to luncheon with Eddie Goldmark of the Goldmark films who is always wanting me to sign a contract to go into the cinema. Because Mr Goldmark is madly in love with Dorothy and Dorothy is always wanting me to go back in the cinema because Dorothy says that she will go if I will go.

April 6th: Well I finally wrote Mr Eisman that I was going to get married and it seems that he is coming on at once as he would probably like to give me his advice. Getting married is really quite serious and Gerry talks to me for hours and hours about it. I mean he never seems to get tired of talking and he does not seem to even want to go to shows or dance or do anything else but talk, and if I don't have something to put my mind on soon I will scream.

April 7th: Well Mr Eisman arrived this morning and he and I had quite a long talk, and after all I think he is right. Because here is the first real opportunity I have ever really had. I mean to go to Paris to broaden out and improve my writing, and why should I give it up to marry an author, where he is the whole thing and all I would be would be the wife of Gerald Lamson? And on top of that I would have to be dragged into the scandal of a divorce court and get my name smirched. So Mr Eisman said that opportunities come too seldom in a girl's life for me to give up the first one I have really ever had. So I am sailing for France and London on Tuesday and taking Dorothy with me and Mr Eisman says that he will see us there later. So Dorothy knows all the ropes and she can get along in Paris just as though she knew French and besides she knows a French gentleman who was born and raised there, and speaks it like a native and knows Paris like a book. And Dorothy says that when we get to London nearly everybody speaks English anyway. So it is quite lucky Mr Lamson is out lecturing in Cincinnati and he will not be back until Wednesday and I can send him a letter and tell him that I have to go to Europe now but I will see him later perhaps. So anyway I will be spared listening to any more of his depressing conversation. So Mr Eisman gave me quite a nice string of pearls and he gave Dorothy a diamond pin and we all went to the Colony for dinner and we all went to a show and supper at the Trocadero and we all spent quite a pleasant evening.

Milt Gross

ANY COLLECTION of American humour would scarcely be complete without a page or two in the dialect of New York's East side. There are several examples to choose from. Arthur Kober's stories of life in the Bronx have gained him a good reputation in the USA, and Milt Gross rather more fancifully writes fairy tales for his 'Nize Baby', a child who needs, like children everywhere, a helpful commentary at mealtimes. Many American slang words, like 'mazuma' (money), are of Yiddish origin, and at one time the Yiddish idiom in humour was fashionable on the New York stage. It's interesting to compare the style of this Midas fairy-tale with the magnificent Mr Kaplan.

❧

FERRY-TAIL FROM KEENG MITAS FOR NIZE BABY

OOhoo, nize baby, itt opp all de Cheeken Zoop so mamma'll gonna tell you a Ferry-Tail from Keeng Mitas. Wance oppon a time was a werry, werry reech Keeng from de name from Keeng Mitas. Sotch a welth wot he hed!—wot it would make J. P. Morgan witt Hanry Fudd witt John D. Rockefeller dey should look like puppers. (Nize baby, take anodder spoon cheeken zoop—)

So instat from bing setisfite and contempted—he becrutched yat averbody helse wot dey possassed, und he was only trying how he could incriss yat wot he had (mmmm-dot griddy ting). So a whole time he was hudding opp de moneh und glutting yat from it like a miser. So wan day he was wukking opp und don in de godden so he was tinking so, 'Hm—wot could I do dot I should hev it ivvin more yat from wot I got?' (mmm—dot salfish critchure). So he was interropted by a leedle Ferry wot it was stending in de front from him witt a Megic Want.

So de Ferry sad, "You Keeng Mitas???"

So de Keeng sad, "So wot is??"

So de Ferry sad, "I'm a Ferry wot I could grent you wot annyting wot you'll weesh so'll be foolfeeled de weesh!!!" So de Keeng sad, "Wot kind bunco-steerage game you call dees, ha? You got some goot-for-notting Hoil Stocks wot you want to sell it, ha, maybe? Odder a petent carpet-swipper, odder maybe a phony Gold mine yat, ha! Try batter by Ole Keeng Cole, not by me—Goot hefternoon!!"

So de Ferry sad, "Hm—you a werry septical poison, ha? Soppose wot you geeve me a hopportunity I should con-weence you?"

So de Keeng sad, "Ho K. I weesh wot averyting wot I toch it, it should toin into gold."

So he was holding in de hend a spectre, so de Feery gave him a tree times a tep witt de megic want—so he gave a look—so it was by him a solit gold spectre in de hand!!—Noo, noo! —So don't esk!!!

So de Keeng was dencing witt jomping witt lipping witt bonding witt prencing from joy. You should see wot he was deshing hitter witt titter—opp witt don, high witt low—beck witt futt, to witt frau—wot he was touching averyting on wheech he put on de hends. So his Wessel sad, "Is goot now?" So de Keeng sad, "Yeh, is goot bot look a hincome-tax I'll gonna have und'll be mine lock yat wot I'll gat maybe tomorrow roomateezum in de hends." (MMMmmm—dot apparitious ting.)

So it came gredually deener-time so de Keeng was werry hongry so he set don he should itt opp a hoyster. So so soon wot he toched de hoyster it became solit gold!! So he said, "Hm—Wott's dees?" So he tried he should ketch in queek a potato in de mout no one should see, so so soon wot he stodded he should chew it, it became solit gold wot it broke him two teet witt a cron witt a heff from de breedge—woik yat besites wot it was werry hot so it made him yat a bleesters on de tong!!

So he sad—"Hm!—Is a seerous preposition. It simms wot I'll have to employ stragedy." So he sad to de Wessel, "I'll gonna stend witt de mout open—So you'll put in a bean-shooter a hepple, wot you'll shoot it, it should go in mine mout wot I'll swallow it queek it shouldn't toch me." So de Wessel compiled gredually witt de requast, bot he was a werry poor moxman, so instat from de Keeng's mout, it went in de

had, wot it became immiditly gold wot it gave him sotch a knock wot he had almost conclusion from de brain.

So was a werry cricketal situation—wot de Keeng sad, "Hm, so it rimmains wot I'll gonna hev to leeve maybe a whole life on gold-feesh, Ha!!" So it was gredually all kind from trobles!! It came de night so he stodded in he should ondrass so it was dere by him a pair from 18 carrot Bivvy Dizz wot de wessels had to ondrass him yat witt a can-uppener. So one day he was wukking opp witt don so it came ronning over to heem his leedle dudder—Hm, deed she was a switt child! So he was so epsom minded, dot dope, wot he put on her head de hend he should toch her so she became solit gold. Yi yi yi yi—So you should see a griff from a remuss wot it was by de Keeng—mmm!!! Deed he was sowry!!! witt meeserable witt donhotted—witt rependant—wot he was wipping beeterly.

So it gredually appeared in de front from him de Ferry witt de Megic Want so he sad, "Goot Monnink, Keeng, How is by you de Gold Rosh???" So de Keeng gave sotch a grun from meesery wot it toched de Ferry's hott—so he sad, "You'll gonna be steengy witt griddy witt salfish anny more?"

So de Keeng sad "No."

"You'll gonna dunnate maybe itch year something to de Meelk Fond?"

"Yeh."

"Wid de Selwation Ommy?"

"Yeh."

"Wid de Uffan's Home?"

"Yeh."

"So you'll gonna refumm, ha?"

"Yeh."

"In odder woids you'll gonna be from now on a deeference indiwijial halltogadder?"

"Cruss mine hott!"

So de Ferry gave him tree times a tep witt de Megic Want so dere it was stending in de front of him de leedle dudder jost like new, wot dey leeved heppily hever hefter.

(Hm—Sotch a dollink baby—ate opp all de cheeken zoop!)

Clarence Day

AMERICAN AUTHORS are apt to rush into print with stories of family life. The author of *Life with Father* was a long time thinking out what to say about his remarkable parent, and Mr Day, Sr., did not become a public figure until 1932. But as the mature and discerning stories unfolded, people agreed that Clarence had done well to wait that long.

In real life, Father had been a prosperous Wall Street banker. *His* father had founded the New York *Sun*, but Clarence at first refused either a business or journalistic career, and joined the US Navy. He was an invalid during the last thirty years of his life, and died while *Life with Father* was still in manuscript. Four years later, the character of Father, in a dramatized version of the book, trod the stage, rather like a comic Moulton Barrett.

Clarence Day's fame rests on these tales, but his drawings with their accompanying verses are the real collectors' pieces. His subjects were protoplasmic, his style like G. K. Chesterton, with an echo of William Blake. And underneath would be a terse line or two by way of commentary.

> The heart of man is capable of
> Forty ridiculous kinds of love,
> While the heart of woman is just an ocean
> Of jealous, immoderate, damp devotion.

❖

FATHER WAKES UP THE VILLAGE

One of the most disgraceful features of life in the country, Father often declared, was the general inefficiency and slackness of small village tradesmen. He said he had originally supposed that such men were interested in business, and that that was why they had opened their shops and sunk capital in them, but no, they never used them for anything but gossip and sleep. They took no interest in civilized ways. Hadn't heard of them probably. He said that of course if he were camping out on the veldt or the tundra, he would expect few conveniences in the neighbourhood and would do his best to forgo them, but why should he be confronted with the wilds twenty miles from New York?

Usually, when Father talked this way, he was thinking of ice. He strongly objected to spending even one day of his life without a glass of cold water beside his plate at every meal. There was never any difficulty about this in our home in the city. A great silver ice-water pitcher stood on the sideboard all day, and when Father was home its outer surface was frosted with cold. When he had gone to the office, the ice was allowed to melt sometimes, and the water got warmish, but never in the evening, or on Sundays, when Father might want some. He said he liked water, he told us it was one of Nature's best gifts, but he said that like all her gifts it was unfit for human consumption unless served in a suitable manner. And the only right way to serve water was icy cold.

It was still more important that each kind of wine should be served at whatever the right temperature was for it. And kept at it, too. No civilized man would take dinner without wine, Father said, and no man who knew the first thing about it would keep his wine in hot cellars. Mother thought this was a mere whim of Father's. She said he was fussy. How about people who lived in apartments, she asked him, who didn't have cellars? Father replied that civilized persons didn't live in apartments.

One of the first summers that Father ever spent in the country, he rented a furnished house in Irvington on the Hudson, not far from New York. It had a garden, a stable, and one or two acres of woods, and Father arranged to camp out there with many misgivings. He took a train for New York every morning at eight-ten, after breakfast, and he got back between five and six, bringing anything special we might need along with him, such as a basket of peaches from the city, or a fresh package of his own private coffee.

Things went well until one day in August the ice-man didn't come. It was hot, he and his horses were tired, and he hated to come to us anyhow because the house we had rented was perched up on top of a hill. He said afterwards that on this particular day he had not liked the idea of making his horses drag the big ice-wagon up that sharp and steep road to sell us fifty cents' worth of ice. Besides, all his ice was gone anyhow —the heat had melted it on him. He had four or five other good reasons. So he didn't come.

Father was in town. The rest of us waited in astonishment wondering what could be the matter. We were so used to the regularity and punctilio of life in the city that it seemed unbelievable to us that the ice-man would fail to appear. We discussed it at lunch. Mother said that the minute he arrived she would have to give him a talking to. After lunch had been over an hour and he still hadn't come, she got so worried about what Father would say that she decided to send to the village.

There was no telephone, of course. There were no motors. She would have liked to spare the horse if she could, for he had been worked hard that week. But as this was a crisis, she sent for Morgan, the coachman, and told him to bring up the dog-cart.

The big English dog-cart arrived. Two of us boys and the coachman drove off. The sun beat down on our heads. Where the heavy harness was rubbing Brownie's coat, he broke out into a thick, whitish lather. Morgan was sullen. When we boys were along he couldn't take off his stiff black high hat or unbutton his thick, padded coat. Worse still, from his point of view, he couldn't stop at a bar for a drink. That was why Mother had sent us along with him, of course, and he knew it.

We arrived at the little town after a while and I went into the Coal & Ice Office. A wiry-looking old clerk was dozing in a corner, his chair tilted back and his chin resting on his dingy shirt-front. I woke this clerk up. I told him about the crisis at our house.

He listened unwillingly, and when I had finished he said it was a very hot day.

I waited. He spat. He said he didn't see what he could do, because the ice-house was locked.

I explained earnestly that this was the Day family and that something must be done right away.

He hunted around his desk a few minutes, found his chewing tobacco, and said, "Well, sonny, I'll see what I can do about it."

I thanked him very much, as that seemed to me to settle the matter. I went back to the dog-cart. Brownie's check-rein had been unhooked, and he stood with his head hanging down. He looked sloppy. It wouldn't have been so bad with a buggy, but a slumpy horse in a dog-cart can look pretty awful. Also, Morgan was gone. He reappeared soon, coming out of a side door down the street, buttoning up his coat, but with his hat tilted back. He looked worse than the horse.

We checked up the weary animal's head again and drove slowly home. A hot little breeze in our rear moved our dust along with us. At the foot of the hill, we boys got out, to spare Brownie our extra weight. We unhooked his check-rein again. He dragged the heavy cart up.

Mother was sitting out on the piazza. I said the ice would come soon now. We waited.

It was a long afternoon.

At five o'clock, Brownie was hitched up again. The coachman and I drove back to the village. We had to meet Father's train. We also had to break the bad news to him that he would have no ice-water for dinner, and that there didn't seem to be any way to chill his Rhine wine.

The village was as sleepy as ever, but when Father arrived and learned what the situation was, he said it would have to wake up. He told me that he had had a long trying day at the office, the city was hotter than the Desert of Sahara, and he was completely worn out, but that if any ice-man imagined for a moment he could behave in that manner, he, Father, would take his damned head off. He strode into the Coal & Ice Office.

When he came out, he had the clerk with him, and the clerk had put on his hat and was vainly trying to calm Father down. He was promising that he himself would come with the ice-wagon if the driver had left, and deliver all the ice we could use, and he'd be there inside an hour.

Father said, "Inside of an hour be hanged, you'll have to come quicker than that."

The clerk got rebellious. He pointed out that he'd have to go to the stables and hitch up the horses himself, and then get someone to help him hoist a block of ice out of the ice-house. He said it was 'most time for his supper and he wasn't used to such work. He was only doing it as a favour to Father. He was just being neighbourly.

Father said he'd have to be neighbourly in a hurry, because he wouldn't stand it, and he didn't know what the devil the ice company meant by such actions.

The clerk said it wasn't his fault, was it? It was the driver's.

This was poor tactics, of course, because it wound Father up again. He wasn't interested in whose fault it was, he said. It was everybody's. What he wanted was ice and plenty of it, and he wanted it in time for his dinner. A small crowd which had collected by this time listened admiringly as Father shook his finger at the clerk and said he dined at six-thirty.

The clerk went loping off towards the stables to hitch up the big horses. Father waited till he'd turned the corner.

Followed by the crowd, Father marched to the butcher's.

After nearly a quarter of an hour, the butcher and his assistant came out, unwillingly carrying what seemed to be a coffin, wrapped in a black mackintosh. It was a huge cake of ice.

Father got in, in front, sat on the box seat beside me, and took up the reins. We drove off. The coachman was on the rear seat, sitting back-in-back to us, keeping the ice from sliding out with the calves of his legs. Father went a few doors up the street to a little house-furnishings shop and got out again.

I went in the shop with him this time. I didn't want to miss any further scenes of this performance. Father began proceedings by demanding to see all the man's ice-boxes. There were only a few. Father selected the largest he had. Then, when the sale seemed arranged, and when the proprietor was smiling broadly with pleasure at this sudden windfall, Father said he was buying that refrigerator only on two conditions.

The first was that it had to be delivered at his home before dinner. Yes, now. Right away. The shopkeeper explained over and over that this was impossible, but that he'd have it up the next morning, sure. Father said no, he didn't want it the next morning, he had to have it at once. He added that he dined at six-thirty, and that there was no time to waste.

The shopkeeper gave in.

The second condition, which was then put to him firmly, was staggering. Father announced that that ice-box must be delivered full of ice.

The man said he was not in the ice business.

Father said, "Very well then. I don't want it."

The man said obstinately that it was an excellent ice-box.

Father made a short speech. It was the one that we had heard so often at home about the slackness of village tradesmen, and he put such strong emotion and scorn in it that his voice rang through the shop. He closed it by saying, "An icebox is of no use to a man without ice, and if you haven't the enterprise, the gumption, to sell your damned goods to a customer who wants them delivered in condition to use, you had better shut up your shop and be done with it. Not in the ice business, hey? You aren't in business at all!" He strode out.

The dealer came to the door just as Father was getting into the dog-cart, and called out anxiously, "All right, Mr Day. I'll get the refrigerator filled for you and send it up right away."

Father drove quickly home. A thunderstorm seemed to be brewing and this had waked Brownie up, or else Father was putting some of his own supply of energy into him. The poor old boy probably needed it as again he climbed the steep hill. I got out at the foot, and as I walked along behind I saw that Morgan was looking kind of desperate, trying to sit in the correct position with his arms folded while he held in the ice with his legs. The big cake was continually slipping and sliding around under the seat and doing its best to plunge out. It had bumped against his calves all the way home. They must have got good and cold.

When the dog-cart drew up at our door, Father remained seated a moment while Morgan, the waitress, and I pulled and pushed at the ice. The mackintosh had come off it by this time. We dumped it out on the grass. A little later, after Morgan had unharnessed and hurriedly rubbed down the horse, he ran back to help us boys break the cake up, rush the chunks around to the back door, and cram them into the ice-box while Father was dressing for dinner.

Mother had calmed down by this time. The Rhine wine was cooling. "Don't get it too cold," Father called.

Then the ice-man arrived.

The old clerk was with him, like a warden in charge of a prisoner. Mother stepped out to meet them, and at once gave the ice-man the scolding that had been waiting for him all day.

The clerk asked how much ice we wanted. Mother said we

didn't want any now. Mr Day had brought home some, and we had no room for more in the ice-box.

The ice-man looked at the clerk. The clerk tried to speak, but no words came.

Father put his head out of the window. "Take a hundred pounds, Vinnie," he said. "There's another box coming."

A hundred-pound block was brought into the house and heaved into the washtub. The waitress put the mackintosh over it. The ice-wagon left.

Just as we all sat down to dinner, the new ice-box arrived, full.

Mother was provoked. She said, "Really, Clare!" crossly. "Now what am I to do with that piece that's waiting out in the washtub?"

Father chuckled.

She told him he didn't know the first thing about keeping house, and went out to the laundry with the waitress to tackle the problem. The thunderstorm broke and crashed. We boys ran around shutting the windows upstairs.

Father's soul was at peace. He dined well, and he had his coffee and cognac served to him on the piazza. The storm was over by then. Father snuffed a deep breath of the sweet-smelling air and smoked his evening cigar.

"Clarence," he said. "King Solomon had the right idea about these things. 'Whatsoever thy hand findeth to do', Solomon said, 'do thy damndest'."

Mother called me inside. "Whose mackintosh is that?" she asked anxiously. "Katie's torn a hole in the back."

I heard Father saying contentedly on the piazza, "I like plenty of ice."

In ancient time some beasts of prey
Instead of going off on hunts
Would grunt ingratiating grunts
    To lure a meal their way.
To dine on lamb or terrapin
They merely opened wide their jaws
And flattered victims fluttered in
    Their hard capacious maws.
They used a minimum of guile.
They simply wore a winning smile.

Today we're all so civilized
That maws must sometimes be disguised.
A trick moustache, a noble title,
Or something of the sort is vital.
But still the skilful beast of prey
Discovers that the easiest way
To dine on terrapin and lamb
Is seeming not to give a damn.

The parting injunctions
Of mothers and wives
Are one of those functions
That poison their lives.

There's no one near to cheer or hoot,
    But his tunes are freely blown.
Happy the artist who can toot
    Ecstatic and alone.

Damon Runyon

WHATEVER HAPPENED to the Chicago gangsters and the New York underworld? Perhaps they, and it, are still there, but the characters like Dave the Dude, Rosa Midnight, Harry the Horse, and Ropes McGonnigle seem to come from another age, before foreign atom spies took over. There was the time when Damon Runyon's picaresque crew took London by storm, and London still has its gang law. We have always liked sports writers anyhow, and Runyon came to us with a solid reputation for his knowledge of the Game.

He also brought us the historic present, the grammatical feature of the *More than Somewhat* series which never fails to fascinate, and which no one has been able successfully to imitate. It was not a surprise to most of his readers when Runyon turned to films. No doubt the Good Lord fashioned great shambling slobs like William Bendix in their rugged mould for just such a purpose. Then the Guys and Dolls became a famous Broadway and London musical. So perhaps there was something in the underworld after all.

⬦

BLOOD PRESSURE

It is maybe eleven-thirty of a Wednesday night, and I am standing at the corner of Forty-eighth Street and Seventh Avenue, thinking about my blood pressure, which is a proposition I never before think much about.

In fact, I never hear of my blood pressure before this Wednesday afternoon when I go around to see Doc Brennan about my stomach, and he puts a gag on my arm and tells me that my blood pressure is higher than a cat's back, and the idea is for me to be careful about what I eat, and to avoid excitement, or I may pop off all of a sudden when I am least expecting it.

"A nervous man such as you with a blood pressure away up

in the paint cards must live quietly," Doc Brennan says. "Ten bucks, please," he says.

Well, I am standing there thinking it is not going to be so tough to avoid excitement the way things are around this town right now, and wishing I have my ten bucks back to bet it on Sun Beau in the fourth race at Pimlico the next day, when all of a sudden I look up, and who is in front of me but Rusty Charley.

Now if I have any idea Rusty Charley is coming my way, you can go and bet all the coffee in Java I will be somewhere else at once, for Rusty Charley is not a guy I wish to have any truck with whatever. In fact, I wish no part of him. Furthermore, nobody else in this town wishes to have any part of Rusty Charley, for he is a hard guy indeed. In fact, there is no harder guy anywhere in the world. He is a big wide guy with two large hard hands and a great deal of very bad disposition, and he thinks nothing of knocking people down and stepping on their kissers if he feels like it.

In fact, this Rusty Charley is what is called a gorill, because he is known to often carry a gun in his pants pocket, and sometimes to shoot people down as dead as doornails with it if he does not like the way they wear their hats—and Rusty Charley is very critical of hats. The chances are Rusty Charley shoots many a guy in this man's town, and those he does not shoot he sticks with his shiv—which is a knife—and the only reason he is not in jail is because he just gets out of it, and the law does not have time to think up something to put him back in again for.

Anyway, the first thing I know about Rusty Charley being in my neighbourhood is when I hear him saying: "Well, well, well, here we are!"

Then he grabs me by the collar, so it is no use of me thinking of taking it on the lam away from there, although I greatly wish to do so.

"Hello, Rusty," I say, very pleasant. "What is the score?"

"Everything is about even," Rusty says. "I am glad to see you, because I am looking for company. I am over in Philadelphia for three days on business."

"I hope and trust that you do all right for yourself in Philly, Rusty," I say; but his news makes me very nervous, because I am a great hand for reading the papers and I have a pretty good idea what Rusty's business in Philly is. It is only the day before that I see a little item from Philly in the papers about how Gloomy Gus Smallwood, who is a very large operator in the alcohol business there, is guzzled right at his front door.

Of course, I do not know that Rusty Charley is the party who guzzles Gloomy Gus Smallwood, but Rusty Charley is in Philly when Gus is guzzled, and I can put two and two together as well as anybody. It is the same thing as if there is a bank robbery in Cleveland, Ohio, and Rusty Charley is in Cleveland, Ohio, or near there. So I am very nervous, and I figure it is a sure thing my blood pressure is going up every second.

"How much dough do you have on you?" Rusty says. "I am plum broke."

"I do not have more than a couple of bobs, Rusty," I say. "I pay a doctor ten bucks today to find out my blood pressure is very bad. But of course you are welcome to what I have."

"Well, a couple of bobs is no good to high-class guys like you and me," Rusty says. "Let us go to Nathan Detroit's crap game and win some money."

Now, of course, I do not wish to go to Nathan Detroit's crap game; and if I do wish to go there I do not wish to go with Rusty Charley, because a guy is sometimes judged by the company he keeps, especially around crap games, and Rusty Charley is apt to be considered bad company. Anyway, I do not have any dough to shoot craps with, and if I do have dough to shoot craps with, I will not shoot craps with it at all, but will bet it on Sun Beau, or maybe take it home and pay off some of the overhead around my joint, such as rent.

Furthermore, I remember what Doc Brennan tells me about avoiding excitement, and I know there is apt to be excitement around Nathan Detroit's crap game if Rusty Charley goes there, and may be run my blood pressure up and cause me to pop off very unexpected. In fact, I already feel my blood jumping more than somewhat inside me, but naturally I am not going to give Rusty Charley any argument, so we go to Nathan Detroit's crap game.

This crap game is over a garage in Fifty-second Street this particular night, though sometimes it is over a restaurant in Forty-seventh Street, or in back of a cigar store in Forty-fourth Street. In fact, Nathan Detroit's crap game is apt to be anywhere, because it moves around every night, as there is no sense in a crap game staying in one spot until the coppers find out where it is.

So Nathan Detroit moves his crap game from spot to spot, and citizens wishing to do business with him have to ask where he is every night; and of course almost everybody on Broadway knows this, as Nathan Detroit has guys walking up and down and around and about, telling the public his address, and giving out the password for the evening.

Well, Jack the Beefer is sitting in an automobile outside the garage in Fifty-second Street when Rusty Charley and I come along, and he says "Kansas City", very low, as we pass, this being the password for the evening; but we do not have to use any password whatever when we climb the stairs over the garage, because the minute Solid John, the doorman, peeks out through his peephole when we knock, and sees Rusty Charley with me, he opens up very quick indeed, and gives us a big castor-oil smile, for nobody in this town is keeping doors shut on Rusty Charley very long.

It is a very dirty room over the garage, and full of smoke, and the crap game is on an old pool table; and around the table, and packed in so close you cannot get a knitting-needle between any two guys with a mawl, are all the high shots in town, for there is plenty of money around at this time, and many citizens are very prosperous. Furthermore, I wish to say there are some very tough guys around the table, too, including guys who will shoot you in the head, or maybe the stomach, and think nothing whatever about the matter.

In fact, when I see such guys as Harry the Horse, from Brooklyn, and Sleepout Sam Levinsky, and Lone Louie, from Harlem, I know this is a bad place for my blood pressure, for these are very tough guys indeed, and are known as such to one and all in this town.

But there they are wedged up against the table with Nick the Greek, Big Nig, Grey John, Okay Okun, and many other high shots, and they all have big coarse G notes in their hands which they are tossing around back and forth as if these G notes are nothing but pieces of waste paper.

On the outside of the mob at the table are a lot of small operators who are trying to cram their fists in between the high shots now and then to get down a bet, and there are also guys present who are called Shylocks, because they will lend you dough when you go broke at the table, on watches or rings, or maybe cufflinks, at very good interest.

Well, as I say, there is no room at the table for as many as one more very thin guy when we walk into the joint, but Rusty Charley lets out a big hello as we enter, and the guys all look around, and the next minute there is space at the table big enough not only for Rusty Charley but for me, too. It really is quite magical the way there is suddenly room for us when there is no room whatever for anybody when we come in.

"Who is the gunner?" Rusty Charley asks, looking all around.

"Why, you are, Charley," Big Nig, the stick man in the game, says very quick, handing Charley a pair of dice, although afterward I hear that his pal is right in the middle of a roll trying to make nine when we step up to the table. Everybody is very quiet, just looking at Charley. Nobody pays any attention to me, because I am known to one and all as a guy who is just around, and nobody figures me in on any part of Charley, although Harry the Horse looks at me once in a way that I know is no good for my blood pressure, or for anybody else's blood pressure as far as this goes.

Well, Charley takes the dice and turns to a little guy in a derby hat who is standing next to him scrooching back so Charley will not notice him, and Charley lifts the derby hat off the little guy's head, and rattles the dice in his hand and chucks them into the hat and goes "Hah!" like crap shooters always do when they are rolling the dice. Then Charley peeks into the hat and says "Ten", although he does not let anybody else look in the hat, not even me, so nobody knows if Charley throws a ten, or what.

But, of course, nobody around is going to up and doubt that Rusty Charley throws a ten, because Charley may figure it is the same thing as calling him a liar, and Charley is such a guy as is apt to hate being called a liar.

Now Nathan Detroit's crap game is what is called a head-and-head game, although some guys call it a fading game, because the guys bet against each other rather than against the bank, or house. It is just the same kind of game as when two guys get together and start shooting craps against each other, and Nathan Detroit does not have to bother with a regular

74

crap table and a layout such as they have in gambling houses. In fact, about all Nathan Detroit has to do with the game is to find a spot, furnish the dice, and take his percentage, which is by no means bad.

In such a game as this there is no real action until a guy is out on a point, and then the guys around commence to bet he makes this point, or that he does not make this point, and the odds in any country in the world that a guy does not make a ten with a pair of dice before he rolls seven is 2 to 1.

Well, when Charley says he rolls ten in the derby hat nobody opens their trap, and Charley looks all around the table, and all of a sudden he sees Jew Louie at one end, although Jew Louie seems to be trying to shrink himself up when Charley's eyes light on him.

"I will take the odds for five C's," Charley says, "and Louie, you get it"—meaning he is letting Louie bet him $1000 to $500 that he does not make his ten.

Now Jew Louie is a small operator at all times and more of a Shylock than he is a player, and the only reason he is up there against the table at all at this moment is because he moves up to lend Nick the Greek some dough; and ordinarily there is no more chance of Jew Louie betting a thousand to five hundred on any proposition whatever than there is of him giving his dough to the Salvation Army, which is no chance at all. It is a sure thing he will never think of betting a thousand to five hundred a guy will not make ten with the dice, and when Rusty Charley tells Louie he has such a bet, Louie starts trembling all over.

The others around the table do not say a word, and so Charley rattles the dice again in his duke, blows on them, and chucks them into the derby hat and says "Hah!" But, of course, nobody can see in the derby hat except Charley, and he peeks in at the dice and says "Five". He rattles the dice once more and chucks them into the derby and says "Hah!" and then after peeking into the hat at the dice he says "Eight". I am commencing to sweat for fear he may heave a seven in the hat and blow his bet, and I know Charley has no five C's to pay off with, although, of course, I also know Charley has no idea of paying off no matter what he heaves.

On the next chuck, Charley yells "Money!"—meaning he finally makes his ten, although nobody sees it but him; and he reaches out his hand to Jew Louie, and Jew Louie hands him a big fat G note, very, very slow. In all my life I never see a sadder-looking guy than Louie when he is parting with his dough. If Louie has any idea of asking Charley to let him see the dice in the hat to make sure about the ten, he does not speak about the matter, and as Charley does not seem to wish to show the ten around, nobody else says anything either, probably figuring Rusty Charley isn't a guy who is apt to let anybody question his word, especially over such a small matter as a ten.

"Well," Charley says, putting Louie's G note in his pocket, "I think this is enough for me tonight," and he hands the derby hat back to the little guy who owns it and motions me to come on, which I am glad to do, as the silence in the joint is making my stomach go up and down inside me, and I know this is bad for my blood pressure. Nobody as much as opens his face from the time we go in until we start out, and you will be surprised how nervous it makes you to be in a big crowd with everybody dead still, especially when you figure it a spot that is liable to get hot any minute. It is only just as we got to the door that anybody speaks, and who is it but Jew Louie, who pipes up and says to Rusty Charley like this:

"Charley," he says, "do you make it the hard way?"

Well, everybody laughs, and we go on out, but I never hear myself whether Charley makes his ten with a six and a four, or with two fives—which is the hard way to make a ten with the dice—although I often wonder about the matter afterward.

I am hoping that I can now get away from Rusty Charley and go on home, because I can see he is the last guy in the world to have around a blood pressure, and, furthermore, that people may get the wrong idea of me if I stick around with him, but when I suggest going to Charley, he seems to be hurt.

"Why," Charley says, "you are a fine guy to be talking of quitting a pal just as we are starting out. You will certainly stay with me because I like company, and we will go down to Ikey the Pig's and play stuss. Ikey is an old friend of mine, and I owe him a complimentary play."

Now, of course, I do not wish to go to Ikey the Pig's, because it is a place away downtown, and I do not wish to play stuss, because this is a game which I am never able to figure out myself, and, furthermore, I remember Doc Brennan says

I ought to get a little sleep now and then; but I see no use in hurting Charley's feelings, especially as he is apt to do something drastic to me if I do not go.

So he calls a taxi, and we start downtown for Ikey the Pig's, and the jockey who is driving the short goes so fast that it makes my blood pressure go up a foot to a foot and a half from the way I feel inside, although Rusty Charley pays no attention to the speed. Finally I stick my head out the window and ask the jockey to please take it a little easy, as I wish to get where I am going all in one piece, but the guy only keeps busting along.

We are at the corner of Nineteenth and Broadway when all of a sudden Rusty Charley yells at the jockey to pull up a minute, which the guy does. Then Charley steps out of the cab and says to the jockey like this:

"When a customer asks you to take it easy, why do you not be nice and take it easy? Now see what you get."

And Rusty Charley hauls off and clips the jockey a punch on the chin that knocks the poor guy right off the seat into the street, and then Charley climbs into the seat himself and away we go with Charley driving, leaving the guy stretched out as stiff as a board. Now Rusty Charley once drives a short for a living himself, until the coppers get an idea that he is not always delivering his customers to the right address, especially such as may happen to be drunk when he gets them, and he is a pretty fair driver, but he only looks one way, which is straight ahead.

Personally, I never wish to ride with Charley in a taxicab under any circumstances, especially if he is driving, because he certainly drives very fast. He pulls up a block from Ikey the Pig's, and says we will leave the short there until somebody finds it and turns it in, but just as we are walking away from the short up steps a copper in uniform and claims we cannot park the short in this spot without a driver.

Well, Rusty Charley just naturally hates to have coppers give him any advice, so what does he do but peek up and down the street to see if anybody is looking, and then haul off and clout the copper on the chin, knocking him bow-legged. I wish to say I never see a more accurate puncher than Rusty Charley because he always connects with that old button. As the copper tumbles, Rusty Charley grabs me by the arm and

77

starts me running up a side street, and after we go about a block we dodge into Ikey the Pig's.

It is what is called a stuss house, and many prominent citizens of the neighbourhood are present playing stuss. Nobody seems any too glad to see Rusty Charley, although Ikey the Pig lets on he is tickled half to death. This Ikey the Pig is a short, fat-necked guy who will look very natural at New Year's, undressed, and with an apple in his mouth, but it seems he and Rusty Charley are really old-time friends, and think fairly well of each other in spots.

But I can see that Ikey the Pig is not so tickled when he finds Charley is there to gamble, although Charley flashes his G note at once, and says he does not mind losing a little dough to Ikey just for old time's sake. But I judge Ikey the Pig knows he is never going to handle Charley's G note, because Charley puts it back in his pocket and it never comes out again even though Charley gets off loser playing stuss right away.

Well, at five o'clock in the morning, Charley is stuck one hundred and thirty G's, which is plenty of money even when a guy is playing on his muscle, and of course Ikey the Pig knows there is no chance of getting one hundred and thirty cents off Rusty Charley, let alone that many thousands. Everybody else is gone by this time and Ikey wishes to close up. He is willing to take Charley's marker for a million if necessary to get Charley out, but the trouble is in stuss a guy is entitled to get back a percentage of what he loses, and Ikey figures Charley is sure to wish this percentage even if he gives a marker, and the percentage will wreck Ikey's joint.

Furthermore, Rusty Charley says he will not quit loser under such circumstances because Ikey is his friend, so what happens but Ikey finally sends out and hires a cheater by the name of Dopey Goldberg, who takes to dealing the game, and in no time he has Rusty Charley even by cheating in Rusty Charley's favour.

Personally, I do not pay much attention to the play, but grab myself a few winks of sleep in a chair in a corner, and the rest seems to help my blood pressure no little. In fact, I am not noticing my blood pressure at all when Rusty Charley and I get out of Ikey the Pig's, because I figure Charley will let me go home and I can go to bed. But although it is six o'clock, and coming on broad daylight, when we leave Ikey's, Charley is still full of zing, and nothing will do him but we must go to a joint that is called the Bohemian Club.

Well, this idea starts my blood pressure going again, because the Bohemian Club is nothing but a deadfall where guys and dolls go when there is positively no other place in town open, and it is run by a guy by the name of Knife O'Halloran, who comes from down around Greenwich Village and is considered a very bad character. It is well known to one and all that a guy is apt to lose his life in Knife O'Halloran's any night, even if he does nothing more than drink Knife O'Halloran's liquor.

But Rusty Charley insists on going there, so naturally I go with him; and at first everything is very quiet and peaceful, except that a lot of guys and dolls in evening clothes, who wind up there after being in the night clubs all night, are yelling in one corner of the joint. Rusty Charley and Knife O'Halloran are having a drink together out of a bottle which Knife carries in his pocket, so as not to get it mixed up with the liquor he sells his customers, and are cutting up old touches of the time when they run with the Hudson Dusters together, when all of a sudden in comes four coppers in plain clothes.

Now these coppers are off duty and are meaning no harm to anybody, and are only wishing to have a dram or two before going home, and the chances are they will pay no attention to Rusty Charley if he minds his own business, although of course they know who he is very well indeed and will take great pleasure in putting the old sleeve on him if they only have a few charges against him, which they do not. So they do not give him a tumble. But if there is one thing Rusty Charley hates it is a copper, and he starts eyeing them from the minute they sit down at a table, and by and by I hear him say to Knife O'Halloran like this:

"Knife," Charley says, "what is the most beautiful sight in the world?"

"I do not know, Charley," Knife says. "What is the most beautiful sight in the world?"

"Four dead coppers in a row," Charley says.

Well, at this I personally ease myself over towards the door, because I never wish to have any trouble with coppers and especially with four coppers, so I do not see everything that comes off. All I see is Rusty Charley grabbing at the big foot which one of the coppers kicks at him, and then everybody seems to go into a huddle, and the guys and dolls in evening dress start squawking, and my blood pressure goes up to maybe a million.

I get outside the door, but I do not go away at once as anybody with any sense will do, but stand there listening to what is going on inside, which seems to be nothing more than a loud noise like ker-bump, ker-bump, ker-bump. I am not afraid there will be any shooting, because as far as Rusty Charley is concerned he is too smart to shoot any coppers, which is the worst thing a guy can do in this town, and the coppers are not likely to start any blasting because they will not wish it to come out that they are in a joint such as the Bohemian Club off duty. So I figure they will all just take it out in pulling and hauling.

Finally the noise inside dies down, and by and by the door opens and out comes Rusty Charley, dusting himself off here and there with his hands and looking very much pleased indeed, and through the door before it flies shut again I catch a glimpse of a lot of guys stretched out on the floor. Furthermore, I can still hear guys and dolls hollering.

"Well, well," Rusty Charley says, "I am commencing to think you take the wind on me, and am just about to get mad at you, but here you are. Let us go away from this joint, because they are making so much noise inside you cannot hear yourself think. Let us go to my joint and make my old woman cook us up some breakfast, and then we can catch some sleep. A little ham and eggs will not be bad to take right now."

Well, naturally ham and eggs are appealing to me no little at this time, but I do not care to go to Rusty Charley's joint. As far as I am personally concerned, I have enough of Rusty Charley to do me a long, long time, and I do not care to enter into his home life to any extent whatever, although to tell the truth I am somewhat surprised to learn he has any such life. I believe I do once hear that Rusty Charley marries one of the neighbours' children, and that he lives somewhere over Tenth Avenue in the Forties, but nobody really knows much about this, and everybody figures if it is true his wife must lead a terrible dog's life.

But while I do not wish to go to Charley's joint, I cannot

very well refuse a civil invitation to eat ham and eggs, especially as Charley is looking at me in a very much surprised way because I do not seem so glad, and I can see that it is not everyone he invites to his joint. So I thank him, and say there is nothing I will enjoy more than ham and eggs such as his old woman will cook for us, and by and by we are walking along Tenth Avenue up around Forty-fifth Street.

It is still fairly early in the morning, and business guys are opening up their joints for the day, and little children are skipping along the sidewalks going to school and laughing tee-hee, and old dolls are shaking bedclothes and one thing and another out of the windows of the tenement houses, but when they spot Rusty Charley and me everybody becomes very quiet indeed, and I can see that Charley is greatly respected in his own neighbourhood. The business guys hurry into their joints, and the little children stop skipping and tee-heeing and go tip-toeing along, and the old dolls yank in their noodles, and a great quiet comes to the street. In fact, about all you can hear is the heels of Rusty Charley and me hitting on the sidewalk.

There is an ice-wagon with a couple of horses hitched to it standing in front of a store, and when he sees the horses Rusty Charley seems to get a big idea. He stops and looks the horses over very carefully, although as far as I can see they are nothing but horses, and big and fat, and sleepy-looking horses at that. Finally Rusty Charley says to me like this:

"When I am a young guy," he says, "I am a very good puncher with my right hand, and often I hit a horse on the skull with my fist and knock it down. I wonder," he says, "if I lose my punch. The last copper I hit back there gets up twice on me."

Then he steps up to one of the ice-wagon horses and hauls off and biffs it right between the eyes with a right-hand smack that does not travel more than four inches, and down goes old Mister Horse to his knees looking very much surprised indeed. I see many a hard puncher in my day including Dempsey when he really can punch, but I never see a harder punch than Rusty Charley gives this horse.

Well, the ice-wagon driver comes busting out of the store all heated up over what happens to his horse, but he cools out the minute he sees Rusty Charley, and goes on back into the store leaving the horse still taking a count, while Rusty Charley and I keep walking. Finally we come to the entrance of a tenement house that Rusty Charley says is where he lives, and in front of this house is a wop with a push-cart loaded with fruit and vegetables and one thing and another, which Rusty Charley tips over as we go into the house, leaving the wop yelling very loud, and maybe cussing us in wop for all I know. I am very glad, personally, we finally get somewhere, because I can feel that my blood pressure is getting worse every minute I am with Rusty Charley.

We climb two flights of stairs, and then Charley opens a door and we step into a room where there is a pretty little red-headed doll about knee high to a flivver, who looks as if she may get out of the hay, because her red hair is flying around every which way on her head, and her eyes seem still gummed up with sleep. At first I think she is a very cute sight indeed, and then I see something in her eyes that tells me this doll, whoever she is, is feeling very hostile to one and all.

"Hello, tootsie," Rusty Charley says. "How about some ham and eggs for me and my pal here? We are all tired out going around and about."

Well, the little red-headed doll just looks at him without saying a word. She is standing in the middle of the floor with one hand behind her, and all of a sudden she brings this hand around, and what does she have in it but a young baseball bat, such as kids play ball with, and which cost maybe two bits; and the next thing I know I hear something go ker-bap, and I can see she smacks Rusty Charley on the side of the noggin with the bat.

Naturally I am great horrified at this business, and figure Rusty Charley will kill her at once, and then I will be in a jam for witnessing the murder and will be held in jail several years like all witnesses to anything in this man's town; but Rusty Charley only falls into a big rocking-chair in a corner of the room and sits there with one hand to his head, saying, "Now hold on tootsie," and "Wait a minute there, honey." I recollect hearing him say, "We have company for breakfast," and then the little red-headed doll turns on me and gives me a look such as I will always remember, although I smile at her very pleasant and mention it is a nice morning.

Finally she says to me like this:

"So you are the trambo who keeps my husband out all night, are you, you trambo?" she says, and with this she starts for me, and I start for the door; and by this time my blood pressure is all out of whack, because I can see that Mrs Rusty Charley is excited more than somewhat. I get my hand on the knob and just then something hits me alongside the noggin, which I afterward figure must be the baseball bat, although I remember having a sneaking idea the roof caves in on me.

How I get the door open I do not know, because I am very dizzy in the head and my legs are wobbling, but when I think back over the situation I remember going down a lot of steps very fast, and by and by the fresh air strikes me, and I figure I am in the clear. But all of a sudden I feel another strange sensation back of my head and something goes plop against my noggin, and I figure at first that maybe my blood pressure runs up so high that it squirts out the top of my bean. Then I peek around over my shoulder just once to see that Mrs Rusty Charley is standing beside the wop peddler's cart snatching fruit and vegetables of one kind and another off the cart and chucking them at me.

But what she hits me with back of the head is not an apple or a peach, or a rutabaga, or a cabbage, or even a casaba melon, but a brickbat that the wop has on his cart to weight down the paper sacks in which he sells his goods. It is this brickbat which makes a lump on the back of my head so big that Doc Brennan thinks it is a tumour when I go to him the next day about my stomach, and I never tell him any different.

"But," Doc Brennan says, when he takes my blood pressure again, "your pressure is down below normal now, and as far as it is concerned you are in no danger whatever. It only goes to show what just a little bit of quiet living will do for a guy," Doc Brennan says. "Ten bucks, please," he says.

Frank Sullivan

IT MAY be that Mr Sullivan will best be remembered by English readers for his descriptions of a weekend at Lady Astor's, or a week in London, when all the current plays were by Noël Coward. Writing as One Who Has Never Been There, Sullivan's description of Cliveden is as satirical as a pre-war cartoon by David Low.

> Lady Astor asked Neville Chamberlain if he would have another helping of asparagus. It sounded innocent enough, but everybody knew that it meant: Would Neville get a place in the Cabinet for General Franco? "By Gad," said Lord Lothian, "I wouldn't be a bit surprised if sooner or later Nancy Astor succeeded in changing the map of Europe."
>
> "Or vice-versa," heckled the spy from His Majesty's Opposition.

Frank Sullivan must be saluted as one of the older generation of American humorists. He can give James Thurber two years, but has still not published the inevitable book of folksy reminiscences—at least, not in this country. In a recent newspaper article, Sullivan (a man other writers like to quote) pointed out that most of the humorists alive in the twenties have since died, and added wistfully of that era—"A halcyon time. There was abandon, but there was also a sense of freedom—of spirit and of speech. The Congressmen and Senators that we freely made fun of . . . now scare American writers to death."

I could add that we ourselves, in the atomic age, have found nothing as lively as the Cliveden Set, and that political satire has been in decline. Frank Sullivan, however, must not be thought of primarily as a sage. In England we know him as the inventor of a Cliché Expert, Mr Arbuthnot, who always had an answer ready, an answer which was clearly a cliché and which revealed the fact that much of our conversation consists of well-worn phrases strung loosely together.

THE CLICHÉ EXPERT TESTIFIES
ON LOVE

Q. Mr Arbuthnot, as an expert in the use of the cliché, are you prepared to testify here today regarding its application in topics of sex, love, matrimony, and so on?

A. I am, Mr Sullivan.

Q. Very good. Now, Mr Arbuthnot, what's love?

A. Love is blind.

Q. Good. What does love do?

A. Love makes the world go round.

Q. Whom does a young man fall in love with?

A. With the Only Girl in the World.

Q. Whom does a young woman fall in love with?

A. With the Only Boy in the World.

Q. When do they fall in love?

A. At first sight.

Q. How?

A. Madly.

Q. They are then said to be?

A. Victims of Cupid's darts.

Q. And he?

A. Whispers sweet nothings in her ear.

Q. Who loves a lover?

A. All the world loves a lover.

Q. Describe the Only Girl in the World.

A. Her eyes are like stars. Her teeth are like pearls. Her lips are ruby. Her cheek is damask, and her form divine.

Q. Haven't you forgotten something?

A. Eyes, teeth, lips, cheek, form—no, sir, I don't think so.

Q. Her hair?

A. Oh, certainly. How stupid of me. She has hair like spun gold.

Q. Very good, Mr Arbuthnot. Now will you describe the Only Man?

A. He is a blond Viking, a he-man, and a square shooter who plays the game. There is something fine about him that rings true, and he has kept himself pure and clean so that when he meets the girl of his choice, the future mother of his children, he can look her in the eye.

Q. How?

A. Without flinching.

Q. Are all the Only Men blond Vikings?

A. Oh, no. Some of them are dark, handsome chaps who have sown their wild oats. This sort of Only Man has a way with a maid, and there is a devil in his eye. But he is not a cad; he would not play fast and loose with an Only Girl's affections. He has a heart of gold. He is a diamond in the rough. He tells the Only Girl frankly about his Past. She understands—and forgives.

Q. And marries him?

A. And marries him.

Q. Why?

A. To reform him.

Q. Does she reform him?

A. Seldom.

Q. Seldom what?

A. Seldom, if ever.

Q. Now, Mr Arbuthnot, when the Only Man falls in love, madly, with the Only Girl, what does he do?

A. He walks on air.

Q. Yes, I know, but what does he do? I mean, what is it he pops?

A. Oh, excuse me. The question, of course.

Q. Then what do they plight?

A. Their troth.

Q. What happens after that?

A. They get married.

Q. What is marriage?

A. Marriage is a lottery.

Q. Where are marriages made?

A. Marriages are made in heaven.

Q. What does the bride do at the wedding?

A. She blushes.

Q. What does the groom do?

A. Forgets the ring.

Q. After the marriage, what?

A. The honeymoon.

Q. Then what?

A. She has a little secret.

Q. What is it?

A. She is knitting a tiny garment.

Q. What happens after that?

A. Oh, they settle down and raise a family and live happily ever afterwards, unless——

Q. Unless what?

A. Unless he is a fool for a pretty face.

Q. And if he is?

A. Then they come to the parting of the ways.

Q. Mr Arbuthnot, thank you very much.

A. But I'm not through yet, sir.

Q. No?

A. Oh, no. There is another side to sex.

Q. There is? What side?

A. The seamy side. There are, you know, men who are wolves in sheep's clothing and there are, alas, lovely women who stoop to folly.

Q. My goodness! Describe these men you speak of, please.

A. They are snakes in the grass who do not place woman upon a pedestal. They are cads who kiss and tell, who trifle with a girl's affections and betray her innocent trust. They are cynics who think that woman is only a woman, but a good cigar is a smoke. Their mottoes are 'Love 'em and leave 'em' and 'Catch 'em young, treat 'em rough, tell 'em nothing'. These cads speak of 'the light that lies in woman's eyes, and lies—and lies—and lies'. In olden days they wore black, curling moustaches, which they twirled, and they invited innocent Gibson girls to midnight suppers, with champagne, at their bachelor apartments, and said, "Little girl, why do you fear me?" Nowadays they have black, patent-leather hair, and roadsters, and they drive up to the kerb and say, "Girlie, can I give you a lift?" They are fiends in human form, who would rob a woman of her most priceless possession.

Q. What is that?

A. Her honour.

Q. How do they rob her?

A. By making improper advances.

Q. What does a woman do when a snake in the grass tries to rob her of her honour?

A. She defends her honour.

Q. How?

A. By repulsing his advances and scorning his embraces.

Q. How does she do that?

A. By saying, "Sir, I believe you forget yourself," or "Please take your arm away," or "I'll kindly thank you to remember I'm a lady," or "Let's not spoil it all".

Q. Suppose she doesn't say any of these things?

A. In that case, she takes the first false step.

Q. Where does the first false step take her?

A. Down the primrose path.

Q. What's the primrose path?

A. It's the easiest way.

Q. Where does it lead?

A. To a life of shame.

Q. What is a life of shame?

A. A life of shame is a fate worse than death.

Q. Now, after lovely woman has stooped to folly, what does she do to the gay Lothario who has robbed her of her most priceless possession?

A. She devotes the best years of her life to him.

Q. Then what does he do?

A. He casts her off.

Q. How?

A. Like an old shoe.

Q. Then what does she do?

A. She goes to their love-nest, then everything goes black before her, her mind becomes a blank, she pulls a revolver, and gives the fiend in human form something to remember her by.

Q. That is called?

A. Avenging her honour.

Q. What is it no jury will do in such a case?

A. No jury will convict.

Q. Mr Arbuthnot, your explanation of the correct application of the cliché in these matters has been most instructive, and I know that all of us cliché-users here will know exactly how to respond hereafter when, during a conversation, sex—when sex—when—ah——

A. I think what you want to say is, "When sex rears its ugly head," isn't it?

Q. Thank you, Mr Arbuthnot. Thank you very much.

A. Thank *you*, Mr Sullivan.

Alexander Woollcott

IF JAMES AGATE had not chosen the title *Ego* for his volumes of personal trivia, Alexander Woollcott might well have used it. The two dramatic critics were much alike, with the same wide knowledge of many subjects, the same irascible, ironic humour, the same following of the faithful literati, the same genius for self-advertisement. And both died in harness, characteristically, Woollcott during a radio programme, Agate correcting proofs.

Perhaps Woollcott took the self-advertisement a degree further. A milestone in the history of histrionics is that for the tour of *The Man Who Came to Dinner* he played the part which S. N. Behrman had written as a parody of him. Woollcott made a number of enemies (among them Tallulah Bankhead), but though he held court, he cannot be said to have courted popularity. I have a feeling that Woollcott, alone, and not in company, gave the best value. He was pacing round Moscow in 1932, and his diary shows a remarkable insight into the Muscovites at a time when the USA and USSR were scarcely even on shouting terms.

It is not really possible to compress Woollcott's sprawling personality into an anthology. One would need a selection of the letters, a handful of notices about plays long dead, a photograph of the critic's face, flaccid and myopic—even a recording of his crochety voice. So I have played for safety in choosing merely the shortest and most famous anecdote from *While Rome Burns*.

⌘

ENTRANCE FEE

This, then, is the story of Cosette and the Saint-Cyrien, much as they tell it (and these many years have been telling it) in the smoky *popotes* of the French army. In the 'nineties, when one heard less ugly babel of alien tongues in the sidewalk cafés, the talk at the apéritif hour was sure to turn sooner or later on

Cosette—Mlle Cosette of the *Variétés*, who was regarded by common consent as the most desirable woman in France. She was no hedged-in royal courtesan, as her possessive fellow-citizens would point out with satisfaction, but a distributed du Barry, the *chère amie* of a republic.

Her origins were misty. Some said she had been born of fisher folk at Plonbazlanec on the Brittany coast. Others preferred the tale that she was the love-child of a famous actress by a very well-known king. In any case, she was now a national legend, and in her pre-eminence the still-bruised French people found in some curious way a balm for their wounded self-esteem. Her photographs, which usually showed her sitting piquantly on a café table, were cut from *L'Illustration* and pinned up in every barracks. Every French lad dreamed of her, and every right-minded French girl quite understood that her sweetheart was saying in effect: "Since I cannot hope to have Cosette, will you come to the river's edge at sundown?" Quite understood, and did not blame him.

Everyone had seen the pictures of Cosette's tiny, vine-hung villa at Saint-Cloud, with its high garden wall and its twittering aviary. And even those for whom that wall was hopelessly high took morbid pride in a persistent detail of the legend which said that no man was ever a guest there for the night who could not bring five thousand francs with him. This was in the 'nineties, mind you, when francs were francs, and men—by a coincidence then more dependable—were men.

The peasant blend of charm and thrift in Cosette filled the cadets at Saint-Cyr with a gentle melancholy. In their twilight hours of relaxation they talked it over, and all thought it a sorrowful thing that, so wretched is the soldier's pittance, not one of those who must some day direct the great *Revanche* would ever carry into battle a memory of the fairest woman in France. For what cadet could hope to raise five thousand francs? It was very sad. But, cried one of their number, his voice shaking, his eyes alight, there were a thousand students at Saint-Cyr, and not one among them so lacking in resource that he could not, if given time, manage to raise at least five francs.

That was how the Cosette Sweepstakes were started. There followed then all the anxious distraction of ways and means, with such Spartan exploits in self-denial, such Damon-and-Pythias borrowings, such flagrant letters of perjured appeal to unsuspecting aunts and godmothers, as Saint-Cyr had never known. But by the appointed time the last man had his, or somebody's, five francs.

The drawing of numbers was well under way when a perplexed instructor stumbled on the proceedings and reported his discovery to the Commandant. When the old General heard the story he was so profoundly moved that it was some time before he spoke.

"The lad who wins the lottery," he said at last, "will be the envy of his generation. But the lad who conceived the idea—ah, he, my friend, will some day be a Marshal of France!"

Then he fell to laughing at the thought of the starry-eyed youngster arriving at the stage door of the *Variétés* with nothing but his youth and his entrance fee. The innocent budget had made no provision for the trip to Paris, none for a carriage, a bouquet, perhaps a supper party. The Commandant said that he would wish to meet this margin of contingency from his own fatherly pocket.

"There will be extras," he said. "Let the young rascal who wins be sent to me before he leaves for Paris."

It was a cadet from the Vendée who reported to the Commandant next afternoon—very trim in his red breeches and blue tunic, his white gloves spotless, his white cockade jaunty, his heart in his mouth. The Commandant said no word to him, but put a little purse of gold Louis in his hand, kissed him on both cheeks in benediction, and stood at his window, moist eyed and chuckling, to watch until the white cockade disappeared down the avenue of trees.

The sunlight, latticed by the jalousies, was making a gay pattern on Cosette's carpet the next morning when she sat up and meditated on the day which stretched ahead of her. Her little cadet was cradled in a sweet dreamless sleep, and it touched her rather to see how preposterously young he was. Indeed, it quite set her thinking of her early days and how she had come up in the world. Then she began speculating on *his* early days, realized with a pang that he was still in the midst of them, and suddenly grew puzzled. Being a woman of action she prodded him.

"Listen, my old one," she said, "how did a cadet at Saint-Cyr ever get hold of five thousand francs?"

Thus abruptly questioned, he lost his head and blurted out the tale of the sweepstakes. Perhaps he felt it could do no harm now, and anyway she listened so avidly, with such flattering little gasps of surprise and such sunny ripples of laughter, that he quite warmed to his story. When he came to the part about the Commandant, she rose and strode up and down, the lace of her peignoir fluttering behind her, tears in her violet eyes.

"Saint-Cyr has paid me the prettiest compliment I have ever known," she said, "and I am the proudest woman in France this day. But surely I must do my part. You shall go back and tell them all that Cosette is a woman of sentiment. When you are an old, old man in the Vendée you shall tell your grandchildren that once in your youth you knew the dearest favours in France, and they cost you not a sou. Not a sou."

At that she hauled open the little drawer where he had seen her lock up the lottery receipts the night before.

"Here," she said, with a lovely gesture. "I give you back your money."

And she handed him his five francs.

Robert Benchley

A FEW MONTHS after Benchley's death, I had occasion to prepare a tribute to him on the radio, with Bea Lillie as narrator. I can hardly believe that it is more than a decade since this gentlest, most urbane, and diffident humorist died. Certainly there has been no one to replace him. My researches took me to the British Museum, in search of a rare early Benchley book. The clerk looked rather crossly at my written request. "Which of these two titles do you want?" he asked.

"It's all one title," I replied, for the book was called *Twenty Thousand Leagues Under the Sea, or David Copperfield*. Well, the British Museum found it, and I think Benchley would have enjoyed the joke.

There were several Benchleys: the Harvard graduate; the pioneer of the *New Yorker*; the wit of the Algonquin Hotel; the champion of the ordinary fallible man struggling to cope with the complexities of civilized life and the early attempts at automation; and the unknown film star who won fame overnight with a miniature masterpiece called *How to Sleep*, and stayed with the cinema till the end, drifting in and out of Hollywood comedies, making brief and nervous appearances, and patting beautiful women on the shoulder in absent-minded sympathy.

'Inseparable my nose and thumb!' wrote Dorothy Parker, once a literary partner of Benchley (they employed the telegraphic address PARKBENCH). But the inseparables were Benchley and Gluyas Williams, whose neat, astringent drawings decorated every Benchley volume since *Love Conquers All* appeared in 1922. And the two of them make a pretty good nose-and-thumb attitude to modern society. Benchley was not a debunker in the manner of H. L. Mencken. He was, rather, a deflater. It is said that outside the Waldorf-Astoria one day he beckoned to a tall, gold-encrusted figure and said "Get me a cab." The figure stiffened, and Benchley was informed that he was speaking to an Admiral. "OK," replied Benchley, unruffled. "Get me a battleship."

He had a genius for parody, and could imitate the Victorian style to perfection. He realized the limitations of his fellow-countrymen in appreciating foreign landscape—and language. But it's as a very abstract and brief chronicler of American times that I like to remember Benchley. This pipe-dream on Dozing might be a prophecy of the Automation Age which he would so much have relished.

⟡

SPORTING LIFE IN AMERICA: DOZING

We Americans are a hardy race, and hardy races need a lot of sleep. 'Sleep, that knits up the ravell'd sleave of care,' Shakespeare has called it, and, except for the fact that it doesn't mean much, it is a pretty good simile. I often think of it myself just as I am dropping off into a light doze: 'Sleep, that sleeves up the ravelled care of . . . knit, that sleep up the shavelled neeve of pfor—pff—prpf—orpffff (*trailing off into a low whistle*).'

One of the most charming manifestations of sleep which we, as a nation, indulge in as a pastime is the Doze. By the Doze I mean those little snatches of sleep which are caught now and then during the day, usually with the collar on and choking slightly, with the head inclined coyly to one side, during which there is a semiconscious attempt to appear as if we were really awake. It is in this department of sleep that we are really at our best.

Of course, there is one form of doze which, to the casual observer or tourist, gives the appearance of legitimate sleep. This is the short doze, or 'quickie', which is taken just after the main awakening in the morning. The alarm rings, or the Lord High Chamberlain taps us on the shoulder (in the absence of a chamberlain a relative will do. And right here I would like to offer for examination that type of sadistic relative who takes actual delight in awakening people. They hover about with ghoulish anticipation until the minute arrives when they may legitimately begin their dirty work, and then, leering unpleasantly, they shake the sleeper roughly with a "Come, come! Time to get up!" and wait right there until he is actually out on the cold floor in his bare feet. There is

94

something radically wrong with such people, and the sooner they are exposed as pathological cases the better it will be for the world.) I'm sorry, I didn't mean to be nasty about it.

At any rate, we are awakened and look at the clock. There are five minutes before it is absolutely necessary to get out of bed. If we leave shaving until night, there might even be fifteen minutes. If we leave dressing until we get to the office, snatching our clothes from the chair and carrying them downtown on our arm, there might even be half an hour more for a good, health-giving nap. Who knows? Perhaps those few minutes of extra sleep might make us just ten times as efficient during the day! That is what we must think of—efficiency. We must sacrifice our petty opinions on the matter and think of the rest of the day and our efficiency. There is no doubt that fifteen minutes' more sleep would do wonders for us, no matter how little we really want to take it.

By the time we have finished this line of argument we are out pretty fairly cold again, but not so cold that we are not conscious of anyone entering the room. We feel that they are going to say: "Come, come, don't go back to sleep again!" and we forestall this warning with a brisk "I know! I know! I'm just thinking!" This is said with one eye partially open and one tiny corner of the brain functioning. The rest of our powers add up to a total loss.

It is one of Nature's wonders how a man can carry on an argument with someone standing beside his bed and still be asleep to all intents and purposes. Not a very good argument, perhaps, and one in which many important words are missing or indistinct, but still an argument. It is an argument, however, which seldom wins, the state of justice in the world being what it is today.

Dozing before arising does not really come within the range of this treatise. What we are concerned with are those little lapses when we are fully dressed, when we fondly believe that no one notices. Riding on a train, for example.

There is the short-distance doze in a day coach, probably the most humiliating form of train sleeping. In this the elbow is rested on the window sill and the head placed in the hand in an attitude of thought. The glass feels very cool on the forehead and we rest it there, more to cool off than anything else. The next thing we know the forehead (carrying the entire head with it) has slid down the length of the slippery pane and we have received a rather nasty bang against the woodwork. They shouldn't keep their glass so slippery. A person is likely to get badly hurt that way.

However, back again goes the forehead against the pane in its original position, with the hand serving more or less as a buffer, until another skid occurs, this time resulting in an angry determination to give the whole thing up entirely and sit up straight in the seat. Some dozers will take four or five slides without whimpering, going back each time for more with apparently undiminished confidence in their ability to see the thing through.

It is a game that you can't beat, however, and the sooner you sit up straight in your seat, the sooner you will stop banging your head.

Dozing in a Pullman chair is not so dangerous, as one does not have the risk of the sliding glass to cope with, but it is even less lovely in its appearance. Here the head is allowed to sink back against the antimacassar—just for a minute to see if the headrest is really as comfortable as it seems. It is then but the work of a minute for the mouth to open slightly and the head to tip roguishly to the right, and there you are—as pretty a picture as one would care to see. You are very lucky if, when you come to and look about, you do not find your neighbours smiling indulgently at some little vagaries of breathing or eccentricities of facial expression which you have been permitting yourself.

The game in all this public dozing is to act, on awakening, as if you had known all along what you were doing. If your neighbours are smiling, you should smile back, as if to say: "Fooled you that time! You thought I was asleep, didn't you?"

If they are not quite so rude as to smile, but look quickly back at their reading on seeing your eyes open, you should assume a brisk, businesslike expression indicating that you have been thinking out some weighty business problem with your eyes closed, and, now that you have at last come on its solution, that it is snap-snap! back to work for you! If, after a furtive look around, you discover that no one has caught you at it, then it will do no harm to give it another try, this time until your collar chokes you into awakening with a strangling gasp.

The collar, however, is not always an impediment to public dozing. In the theatre, for example, a good, stiff dress collar and shirt bosom have been known to hold the sleeper in an upright position when otherwise he might have plunged forward and banged his head on the back of the seat in front.

In my professional capacity as play reviewer I had occasion to experiment in the various ways of sitting up straight and still snatching a few winks of health-giving sleep. I found that by far the safest is to keep one's heavy overcoat on, especially if it is made of some good, substantial material which will hold a sagging torso erect within its folds. With a good overcoat, reinforced by a stiff dress shirt and a high collar, one may even go beyond the dozing stage and sink into a deep, refreshing slumber, and still not be made conspicuous by continual lurchings and plungings. Of course, if you are an uneasy sleeper and given to thrashing about, you will find that even a heavy overcoat will let you down once in a while. But for the average man, who holds approximately the same position after he has gone to sleep, I don't think that this method can go wrong. Its only drawback is that you are likely to get a little warm along about the middle of the second act.

If you don't want to wear your overcoat in the theatre, the next best method is to fold the arms across the chest and brace the chin against the dress collar, exerting a slight upward pressure with the arms against the shirt front. This, however, can be used only for the lightest of dozes, as, once unconsciousness has set in, the pressure relaxes and over you go.

Dozing at a play, however refreshing, makes it a bit difficult to follow the argument on the stage, as occasionally the nap drags itself out into a couple of minutes and you awake to find a wholly fresh set of characters on the scene, or even a wholly fresh scene. This is confusing. It is therefore wise to have someone along with you who will alternate watches with you, dozing when you are awake and keeping more or less alert while you are dozing. In this way you can keep abreast of what has been happening.

This, unfortunately, is impossible in personal conversations. If you slip off into a quick coma late some evening when your *vis-à-vis* is telling you about South America or a new solvent process, it is usually pretty difficult to pick up the thread where you dropped it. You may remember that the last words he was saying were ". . . which is situated at the mouth of the Amazon", but that isn't going to help you much if you come to just as he is asking you: "What would *you* say are?" As in the personal-conversation doze the eyes very seldom completely close (it is more of a turning back of the eyeballs than a closing of the lids) you may escape detection if you have a ready answer for the emergency. I find that "Well, I don't know," said very slowly and deliberately, will fit almost any question that has been asked you. "Yes" and "No" should never be offered as they might make you sound even sillier than you look. If you say: "Well, I—don't—know," it will give you a chance to

collect your wits (what few there are left) and may lead your questioner into answering the thing himself.

At any rate, it will serve as a stall. If there are other people present, some one of them is quite likely to come to your rescue and say something which will tip you off as to the general subject under discussion. From then on, you will have to fight your own battle. I can't help you.

The whole problem is one which calls for a great deal of thought. If we can develop some way in which a man can doze and still keep from making a monkey of himself, we have removed one of the big obstacles to human happiness in modern civilization. It goes without saying that we don't get enough sleep while we are in bed; so we have got to get a little now and then while we are at work or at play. If we can find some way to keep the head up straight, the mouth closed, and just enough of the brain working to answer questions, we have got the thing solved right there.

I am working on it right now, as a matter of fact, but I find it a little difficult to keep awake.

Dorothy Parker

IT MAY be that A. E. Housman is the poet of youth's first dis-illusion, but a literate lad from Shropshire or any other county has only to read straight through a book of short stories called *Here Lies* to be disenchanted for life. Dorothy Parker knows precisely the frailties of a certain stratum of suburban society. Her victims can be anything from newly-weds to dipsomaniac actresses, and it is hard to say why any one of these stories is eligible for an anthology of humour—except that the misfortunes of others tend to amuse us. For Dorothy Parker, you can read John O'Hara. But whichever you read, the result is the same, and your eyes are still smarting.

The stories about Dorothy Parker are nearly as good as her own. She is the hostess who, after speeding a parting guest, murmured, "That woman speaks eighteen languages and can't say No in any of them." She it was who, in a moment of inspired dramatic criticism, described a performance by Katharine Hepburn as running the gamut of emotions from A to B. And she is further credited with putting a notice on her office door to ensure some male visitors one boring afternoon. The notice said 'Gentlemen'.

Parker the prose-writer and Parker the critic have a companion in Parker the poetess. Here, in her collected poems, *Not So Deep as a Well*, there seems to me to be a remarkable splitting of personalities, one wry, one hideously sentimental. It is like receiving a little be-ribboned cellophane box, and not being sure, until the first glance, whether the offering is dewy rose or deadly nightshade.

> Drink and dance and laugh and lie,
> Love, the reeling midnight through!
> For tomorrow, we shall die!
> But, alas, we never do.

In the eighteenth century, Dorothy Parker would have held a salon. As it was, she had to be content to share a tiny office with Robert Benchley. Internal evidence of the work of the two does not clearly show whether Benchley softened Parker or Parker exacerbated Benchley. Eventually, as history knows, Benchley went to Hollywood and Parker went to cover the Civil War in Spain as a newspaper correspondent, and a beautiful friendship was broken up. The only really charitable and appreciative piece of Parker I have ever read is her introduction to Thurber's *Men, Women, and Dogs*, with its insight into the mind of that remarkable artist.

"An odd blend of Little Nell and Lady Macbeth," said Alexander Woollcott once, summing-up on his favourite writer.

❧

YOU WERE PERFECTLY FINE

The pale young man eased himself carefully into the low chair, and rolled his head to the side, so that the cool chintz comforted his cheek and temple.

"Oh, dear," he said. "Oh, dear, oh, dear, oh, dear. Oh."

The clear-eyed girl, sitting light and erect on the couch, smiled brightly at him.

"Not feeling so well today?" she said.

"Oh, I'm great," he said. "Corking, I am. Know what time I got up? Four o'clock this afternoon, sharp. I kept trying to make it, and every time I took my head off the pillow it would roll under the bed. This isn't my head I've got on now. I think this is something that used to belong to Walt Whitman. Oh, dear, oh, dear, oh, dear."

"Do you think maybe a drink would make you feel better?" she said.

"The hair of the mastiff that bit me?" he said. "Oh, no, thank you. Please never speak of anything like that again. I'm through. I'm all, all through. Look at that hand; steady as a humming-bird. Tell me, was I very terrible last night?"

"Oh, goodness," she said, "everybody was feeling pretty high. You were all right."

"Yeah," he said. "I must have been dandy. Is everybody sore at me?"

"Good heavens, no," she said. "Everyone thought you

were terribly funny. Of course, Jim Pierson was a little stuffy, there for a minute at dinner. But people sort of held him back in his chair, and got him calmed down. I don't think anybody at the other tables noticed it at all. Hardly anybody."

"He was going to sock me?" he said. "Oh, Lord. What did I do to him?"

"Why, you didn't do a thing," she said. "You were perfectly fine. But you know how silly Jim gets when he thinks anybody is making too much fuss over Elinor."

"Was I making a pass at Elinor?" he said. "Did I do that?"

"Of course you didn't," she said. "You were only fooling, that's all. She thought you were awfully amusing. She was having a marvellous time. She only got a little tiny bit annoyed just once, when you poured the clam-juice down her back."

"My God," he said. "Clam-juice down that back. And every vertebra a little Cabot. Dear God. What'll I ever do?"

"Oh, she'll be all right," she said. "Just send her some flowers, or something. Don't worry about it. It just isn't anything."

"No, I won't worry," he said. "I haven't got a care in the world. I'm sitting pretty. Oh, dear, oh, dear. Did I do any other fascinating tricks at dinner?"

"You were fine," she said. "Don't be so foolish about it. Everybody was crazy about you. The maître d'hôtel was a little worried because you wouldn't stop singing, but he really didn't mind. All he said was, he was afraid they'd close the place again if there was so much noise. But he didn't care a bit, himself. I think he loved seeing you have such a good time. Oh, you were just singing away, there, for about an hour. It wasn't so terribly loud, at all."

"So I sang," he said. "That must have been a treat. I sang."

"Don't you remember?" she said. "You just sang one song after another. Everybody in the place was listening. They loved it. Only you kept on insisting that you wanted to sing some song about some kind of fusiliers or other, and everybody kept shushing you, and you'd keep trying to start it again. You were wonderful. We were all trying to make you stop singing for a minute, and eat something, but you wouldn't hear of it. My, you were funny."

"Didn't I eat any dinner?" he said.

"Oh, not a thing," she said. "Every time the waiter would offer you something, you'd give it right back to him, because you said that he was your long-lost brother, changed in the cradle by a gypsy band, and that anything you had was his. You had him simply roaring at you."

"I bet I did," he said. "I bet I was comical. Society's Pet, I must have been. And then what happened, after my overwhelming success with the waiter?"

"Why, nothing much," she said. "You took a sort of dislike to some old man with white hair, sitting across the room, because you didn't like his necktie and you wanted to tell him about it. But we got you out, before he got really mad."

"Oh, we got out," he said. "Did I walk?"

"Walk! Of course you did," she said. "You were absolutely all right. There was that nasty stretch of ice on the sidewalk, and you did sit down awfully hard, you poor dear. But good heavens, that might have happened to anybody."

"Oh, sure," he said. "Louisa Alcott or anybody. So I fell down on the sidewalk. That would explain what's the matter with my—— Yes, I see. And then what, if you don't mind?"

"Ah, now, Peter!" she said. "You can't sit there and say you don't remember what happened after that! I did think you were perfectly all right, and all that, but I did know you were feeling pretty gay. But you were so serious, from the time you fell down—I never knew you to be that way. Don't you know, how you told me I had never seen your real self before? Oh, Peter, I just couldn't bear it if you didn't remember that lovely long ride we took together in the taxi! Please, you do remember that, don't you? I think it would simply kill me, if you didn't."

"Oh, yes," he said. "Riding in the taxi. Oh, yes, sure. Pretty long ride, hmm?"

"Round and round and round the park," she said. "Oh, and the trees were shining so in the moonlight. And you said you never knew before that you really had a soul."

"Yes," he said. "I said that. That was me."

"You said such lovely, lovely things," she said. "And I'd never known, all this time, how you had been feeling about me, and I'd never dared to let you see how I felt about you. And then last night—oh, Peter dear, I think that taxi ride was the most important thing that ever happened to us in our lives."

"Yes," he said. "I guess it must have been."

"And we're going to be so happy," she said. "Oh, I just want to tell everybody! But I don't know—I think maybe it would be sweeter to keep it all to ourselves."

"I think it would be," he said.

"Isn't it lovely?" she said.

"Yes," he said, "great."

"Lovely!" she said.

"Look here," he said, "do you mind if I have a drink? I mean, just medicinally, you know; I'm off the stuff for life, so help me. But I think I feel a collapse coming on."

"Oh, I think it would do you good," she said. "You poor boy, it's a shame you feel so awful. I'll go make you a whisky and soda."

"Honestly," he said, "I don't see how you could ever want to speak to me again, after I made such a fool of myself last night. I think I'd better go join a monastery in Tibet."

"You crazy idiot!" she said. "As if I could ever let you go away now! Stop talking like that. You were perfectly fine."

She jumped up from the couch, kissed him quickly on the forehead, and ran out of the room.

The pale young man looked after her and shook his head long and slowly, then dropped it in his damp and trembling hands.

"Oh, dear," he said. "Oh, dear, oh, dear, oh, dear."

MEN

They hail you as their morning star
Because you are the way you are.
If you return the sentiment,
They'll try to make you different;
And once they have you, safe and sound,
They want to change you all around.
Your moods and ways they put a curse on;
They'd make of you another person.
They cannot let you go your gait;
They influence and educate.
They'd alter all that they admired.
They make me sick, they make me tired.

RÉSUMÉ

Razors pain you;
Rivers are damp;
Acids stain you;
And drugs cause cramp.
Guns aren't lawful;
Nooses give;
Gas smells awful;
You might as well live.

NEWS ITEM

Men seldom make passes
At girls who wear glasses.

Leonard Q. Ross

IMMIGRANT HUMOUR from America has a long tradition. One of the most famous nineteenth-century poems, 'Yawcob Strauss', by Charles Follen Adams, was written in the half German dialect of Pennsylvania.

> I haf von funny leedle poy
> > Vot gomes schust to mine knee,
> Der queerest schap, der greatest rogue
> > As efer you did see.
> He runs, und schumps, und schmashes dings
> > In all barts of der house;
> But vot off dat? He vos mine son,
> > Mine leedle Yawcob Strauss.

Leonard Ross's Hyman Kaplan is the modern equivalent. This genial painstaking member of Mr Parkhill's class (American Night Preparatory School for Adults—Preparation for Naturalization) is not someone merely to be laughed at, though his tussles with the language are richly comical. He is thrilled at the prospect of becoming an American citizen, and pays homage to American Presidents and writers, even though he refers to them by such names as Abram Lincohen, Judge Vashington, Mocktain, and Relfvaldo Emerson. He writes his name lovingly, with asterisks between the letters. He goes in for '*dip tinking*'.

In a reference to the work of Milt Gross, Arthur Kober, and Leonard Q. Ross, E. B. White remarks, "It is sympathy, not contempt or derision, that makes their characters live."

❖

MR K*A*P*L*A*N THE MAGNIFICENT

Mr Parkhill had decided that perhaps it might be wise for the class to attempt more *practical* exercises. On a happy thought, he had taken up the subject of letter-writing. He had lectured the students on the general structure of the personal letter: shown them where to put the address, city, date; explained the salutation; talked about the body of the letter; described the final greeting. And now the fruits of Mr Parkhill's labours were being demonstrated. Five students had written the assignment, 'A Letter to a Friend', on the blackboard.

On the whole Mr Parkhill was satisfied. Miss Mitnick had written a straightforward and accurate letter—as might be expected—inviting her friend Sylvia to a surprise party. Mr Norman Bloom had written to someone named Fishbein, describing an exciting day at Coney Island. Miss Rochelle Goldberg had told 'Molly' about a 'bos ride on a bos on 5 av'. Mrs Moskowitz, simple soul, had indulged her fantasies by pretending she was on vacation in 'Miame, Floridal', and had written her husband Oscar to be sure 'the pussy should get each morning milk'. (Apparently Mrs Moskowitz was deeply attached to 'the pussy', for she merely repeated the admonition in several ways all through her epistle, leaving no room for comment on the beauties of 'Miame, Floridal'.) And Mr Hyman Kaplan—Mr Parkhill frowned as he examined the last letter written on the blackboard.

"It's to mine brodder in Varsaw," said Mr Kaplan, smiling in happy anticipation.

Mr Parkhill nodded, rather absently; his eyes were fixed on the board.

"Maybe it vould be easier I should readink de ladder alod," suggested Mr Kaplan delicately.

"'*Letter*', Mr Kaplan," said Mr Parkhill, ever the pedagogue. "Not '*lad*der'."

"Maybe I should readink de *lat*ter?" repeated Mr Kaplan.

"Er—no—no," said Mr Parkhill hastily. "We—er—we haven't much time left this evening. It *is* getting late." He tried to put it as gently as possible, knowing what this harsh deprivation might mean to Mr Kaplan's soul.

Mr Kaplan sighed philosophically, bowing to the tyranny of time.

"The class will study the letter for a few minutes, please," said Mr Parkhill. "Then I shall call for corrections."

I should be telling about mine progriss. In school I am fine
Making som mistakes, netcheral

The class fell into that half-stupor which indicated concentration. Miss Mitnick studied the blackboard with a determined glint in her eye. Mr Pinsky stared at Mr Kaplan's letter with a critical air, saying "Tchk! Tchk!" several times quite professionally. Mrs Moskowitz gazed ceilingward with an exhausted expression. Apparently the vicarious excitements of the class session had been too much for poor Mrs Moskowitz: an invitation to a surprise party, a thrilling day at Coney Island, a Fifth Avenue bus ride, and her own trip to Florida. That was quite a night for Mrs Moskowitz.

And Mr Kaplan sat with his joyous smile unmarred, a study in obvious pride and simulated modesty, like a god to whom mortals were paying homage. First he watched the faces of the students as they wrestled with his handiwork, and found them pleasing. Then he concentrated his gaze on Mr Parkhill. He saw anxious little lines creep around Mr Parkhill's eyes as he read that letter; then a frown—a strange frown, bewildered and incredulous; then a nervous clearing of the throat. Any other student might have been plunged into melancholy by these dark omens, but they only added a transcendental quality to Mr Kaplan's smile.

This was the letter Mr Kaplan had written:

459 E 3 Str.
N.Y.
New York
Octo. 10

Hello Max!!!
 I should be telling about mine progriss. In school I am fine. Making som mistakes, netcheral. Also however doing the hardest xrcises, like the best students the same. Som students is Mitnick, Blum, Moskowitz—no relation Moskowitz in Warsaw. Max! You should absolutel coming to N.Y. and belonging in mine school!

It was at this point, visualizing too vividly *another* Mr Kaplan in the class, that anxious little lines had crept around Mr Parkhill's eyes.

Do you feeling fine? I suppose. Is all ok? You should begin right now learning about ok. Here you got to say ok all the time. ok the wether, ok the potatos, ok the prazident Roosevelt.

At this point the frown—a strange frown, bewildered and incredulous—had marched on to Mr Parkhill's face.

How is darling Fanny! Long should she leave. So long.
With all kinds entusiasm
Your animated brother
H*Y*M*I*E

Mr Kaplan simply could not resist the aesthetic impulse to embellish his signature with those stars; they had almost become an integral part of the name itself.

Mr Parkhill cleared his throat. He felt vaguely distressed.

"Has everyone finished reading?" he asked. Heads nodded in half-hearted assent. "Well, let us begin. Corrections, please."

Mrs Tomasic's hand went up. "Should be 'N.Y.' after 'New York' and 'New York' should be on top of."

"Correct," said Mr Parkhill, explaining the difference and making the change on the board.

"In all places is 'mine' wrong," said Mr Feigenbaum. "It should be 'my'."

Mr Parkhill nodded, happy that someone had caught that most common of Mr Kaplan's errors.

The onslaught went on: the spelling of words, the abbreviations of 'October' and 'street', the tenses of the verbs.

"Mr Kaplan got so many mistakes," began Mr Bloom with hauteur. Mr Bloom was still annoyed because Mr Kaplan had rashly offered to correct the spelling of Coney Island, in Mr Bloom's letter, to "Corney Island, like is pernonced". "He spelled wrong 'progress', 'some', 'natural'. He means 'Long should she *live*'—not 'Long should she *leave*'. That means going away. He even spelled wrong my name!" It was clear from Mr Bloom's indignant tone that this was by far the most serious of Mr Kaplan's many errors. "Is double 'o', not 'u'. I ain't like *som* Blooms!"

With this jealous defence of the honour of the House of Bloom, Mr Bloom looked at Mr Kaplan coolly. If he had thought to see Mr Kaplan chagrined by the barrage of corrections he did not know the real mettle of the man. Mr Kaplan was beaming with delight.

"Honist to Gott, Bloom," said Mr Kaplan with admiration,

"you soitinly improvink in your English to seeink all dese mistakes!"

There was a fine charity in this accolade. It had, however, the subtle purpose of shifting attention from Mr Kaplan's errors to Mr Bloom's progress.

Mr Bloom did not know whether to be pleased or suspicious, whether this was a glowing tribute or the most insidious irony.

"Thenks, Kaplan," he said finally, acknowledging the compliment with a nod, and considered the injuries of 'Corney Island' and 'Blum' expiated.

"I see more mistakes," said Miss Mitnick, intruding an unwelcome note into the happy Kaplan–Bloom *rapport*. Mr Kaplan's eyes gleamed when he heard Miss Mitnick's voice. Here was a foe of a calibre quite different from that of Norman Bloom. " 'Absolutel' should be 'absolutely'. 'Potatoes' has an 'e'. 'Prazident' is wrong; it should be 'e' and 's' and a capital." Miss Mitnick went on and on making corrections. Mr Parkhill transcribed them to the board as swiftly as he could until his wrists began to ache. " 'ok' is wrong, should be 'O.K.'—with *capitals* and *periods*—because it's abbreviation." All through the Mitnick attack Mr Kaplan sat quiet, alert but smiling. There was a supreme confidence in that smile, as if he were waiting for some secret opportunity to send the whole structure that Miss Mitnick was rearing so carefully crashing down upon her head. Miss Mitnick rushed on to the abyss.

"Last," she said, slowing up to emphasize the blow,"*three* exclamation points after 'Max' is wrong. Too many."

"Aha!" cried Mr Kaplan. It was The Opportunity. "Podden me, Mitnick. De odder corractinks you makink is fine, foist-class—even Hau Kay, an' I minn Hau Kay mit *capitals* an' *periods*," he added sententiously. "But batter takink back abot de tree haxclimation points!"

Miss Mitnick blushed, looking to Mr Parkhill for succour.

"Mr Kaplan," began Mr Parkhill with caution, sensing some hidden logic in Mr Kaplan's tone. "A colon is the proper punctuation for the salutation, or a comma. If you *must* use an—er—exclamation point"—he was guarding himself on all fronts—"then, as Miss Mitnick says, *three* are too many."

"For de vay *I'm* fillink abot mine *brodder*?" asked Mr Kaplan promptly. In that question, sublime in its simplicity, Mr Kaplan inferentially accused his detractor of (1) familial ingratitude, (2) trying to come between the strong love of two brothers.

"But, Kaplan," broke in Mr Bloom, jumping into the fray on the side of Miss Mitnick, "*three* exclama——"

"Also, he's mine *fawourite* brodder!" said Mr Kaplan. "For mine fawourite brodder you eskink *vun—lettle—haxclimation point?*" It was an invincible position. "Ha! Dat I give to *strengers!*"

Mr Bloom retired from the field, annihilated. One could hardly expect a man of Mr Kaplan's exquisite sensitivity to give equal deference and love to *strangers* and his favourite brother. Mr Parkhill paused to mobilize his forces.

"How's about 'entusiasm'?" said Miss Mitnick, determined to recover face. "Is spelled wrong—should be 'th'. And 'With all kinds of enthusiasm' is bad for ending a letter."

"Aha!" Mr Kaplan gave his battle-call again. "Maybe *is* de spallink wronk. But not de vay I'm *usink* 'antusiasm', becawss"—he injected a trenchant quality into his voice to let the class get the deepest meaning of his next remark—"becawss *I* write to *mine* brodder in Varsaw *mit real antusiasm!*"

The implication was clear; Miss Mitnick was one of those who, corrupted by the gaudy whirl of the New World, let her brothers starve, indifferently, overseas.

Miss Mitnick bit her lip. Mr Parkhill, trying to look judicious, avoided her eyes.

"Well," began Miss Mitnick yet a third time, desperately, "'animated' is wrong. 'Your *animated* brother, Hymie?' *That's* wrong."

She looked at Mr Parkhill with a plea that was poignant. She dared not look at Mr Kaplan, whose smile had advanced to a new dimension.

"Yes," said Mr Parkhill. "'Animated' is quite out of place in the final greeting."

Mr Kaplan sighed. "I looked op de void 'enimated' *spacial*. It's minnink 'full of life', no? Vell, I falt *planty* full of life ven I vas wridink de ladder."

Miss Mitnick dropped her eyes, the rout complete.

"Mr Kaplan!" Mr Parkhill was left to fight the good fight alone. "You may say 'She had an animated expression' or

'The music has an animated refrain'. But one doesn't say 'animated' about one's *self*."

The appeal to propriety proved successful. Mr Kaplan confessed that perhaps he had overreached himself with 'Your animated brother'.

"Suppose we try another word," suggested Mr Parkhill. "How about 'fond'? 'Your *fond* brother—er—Hyman?'" (He couldn't quite essay 'Hymie'.)

Mr Kaplan half-closed his eyes, gazed into space, and meditated on this moot point. "'Fond', 'fond'," he whispered to himself. He was like a man who had retreated into a secret world searching for his Muse. "'Your fond brodder, Hymie.'" He shook his head. "Podden me," he said apologetically. "It don' have de *fillink*."

"What about 'dear'?" offered Mr Parkhill quickly. "'Your *dear* brother', and so on?"

Once more Mr Kaplan went through the process of testing, judgment, and consultation with his evasive Muse. "'Dear', 'dear'. 'Your dear brodder, Hymie.' Also no." He sighed. "'Dear', it's too *common*."

"What about——"

"Aha!" cried Mr Kaplan suddenly, as the Muse kissed him. His smile was as the sun. "I got him! Poifick! Soch a void!"

The class, to whom Mr Kaplan had communicated some of his own excitement, waited breathlessly. Mr Parkhill himself, it might be said, was possessed of a queer eagerness.

"Yes, Mr Kaplan. What word would you suggest?"

"'Megnificent'!" cried Mr Kaplan.

Admiration and silence fell upon the class like a benediction. 'Your magnificent brother, Hymie.' It was a *coup de maître*, no less. Mr K*A*P*L*A*N the Magnificent.

As if in a trance, the beginners' grade waited for Mr Parkhill's verdict.

And when Mr Parkhill spoke, it was slowly, sadly, aware that he was breaking a magic spell. "N—no, Mr Kaplan. I'm afraid not. 'Magnificent' isn't really—er—appropriate."

The bell rang in the corridors, as if it had withheld its signal until the last possible moment. The class moved into life and toward the door. Mr Norman Bloom went out with Mr Kaplan. Mr Parkhill could hear the last words of their conversation.

"Kaplan," said Mr Bloom enviously, "*how* you fond soch a beautiful woid?"

" 'Megnificent', 'megnificent'," Mr Kaplan murmured to himself wistfully. "Ach! Dat *vas* a beautiful void, ha, Bloom?"

"Believe me!" said Mr Bloom. "*How* you fond soch a woid?"

"By *dip* tinking," said Mr Kaplan.

He strode out like a hero.

Ludwig Bemelmans

TWO AMERICANS, on holiday in the hilly country north of Cannes, once wrote a song in praise of a Small Hotel. They were the exception which proves a well-known rule, that Americans generally prefer a Big Hotel, the larger and more luxurious the better. It is therefore to be expected that they would enjoy revelations of life behind the screens and baize doors of the banqueting department.

All this leads up to Bemelmans' *Hotel Splendide*, his most enduring monument, a vast building whose continental atmosphere, compounded of buhl and borsch, Cartier cabinets and escaliers, could be created in New York as well as in Vienna or Paris. Bemelmans was, in fact, what he calls a 'busboy'; waiter and assistant maître d'hôtel. His descriptions of hotel life, accurate yet fantastic, brought him recognition, and the fact that he was about the only established writer whose drawings could make the cover of the *New Yorker* did nothing to diminish his reputation.

One can see two other sides of the Bemelmans character. He can change the tails and gleaming cuffs of the maître d'hôtel for the rainbow shirt of the American wanderer. I have always envied him his travels in Ecuador, which resulted in *The Donkey Inside*, and wonder what he would make of the shimmering glories of Bangkok. The other characteristic is a lively political sense, a revulsion at the rise of the Nazis, and an unforgettable impression of his ruined Europe immediately after the war.

I once spoke to Bemelmans on the telephone. It was not a long-distance call (we were both in London at the time), but the effort to make contact lasted over a period of several days. No one will be surprised to hear that the switchboard I rang so frequently was at the Savoy. I have always cherished the belief that when he was deemed to be out, Mr Bemelmans had in fact slipped down to the spacious kitchens, to offer the opinion his maître d'hôtel Gabriel would have given on the consistency of the *bisque homard*.

'NO TROUBLE AT ALL'

The world is full of maîtres d'hôtel, many of whom are able, well-informed men. But only one in a hundred thousand is blessed with that rarest, most priceless of qualities so generously evident in Gabriel, the Maître of the Cocofinger Palace Hotel in New York.

We see this peculiar talent in his profile, behind the ear, under 'Detail and Executive Ability'. It is the faculty of 'Anticipation', an astral clairvoyance with which to sense catastrophe, anywhere in the wide realm of his authority. Not only to feel it ahead, but to prepare for it and minimize the effect thereof.

One more look at the graph, and it is evident to anyone why, with such talents, Gabriel has come up, up, up, from the position of third piccolo at the humble 'King Wenceslaus' in Przemysl, through the pantries and over the red carpets of Madame Sacher's, the Negresco, Shepheard's, the Meurice, Claridge's, up to the golden doors of the restaurant of the hotels—the Cocofinger Palace in New York.

Gabriel smokes Dimitrinos, he has ten dozen shirts, Lobb makes his boots, he is driven in a Minerva, thinks in French, his hats come from Habig in Vienna, and both Noël Coward and Cole Porter have asked him who builds his fine tail-coats.

To his many subordinates he speaks through his assistant, one Hector de Malherbes, who at one time worked for Max Reinhardt. (This temperamental aesthetic experience has fitted Malherbes most admirably for his present position.) Between the Maître and Malherbes is perfect, wordless understanding.

Never was proof positive of Gabriel's great talents and of the mute felicity of Malherbes more clearly demonstrated than on the night and day of 25th February 1937.

On that Thursday, at three-fifteen in the afternoon, when the last luncheon guest had left, Gabriel leaned on his desk with its seven drawers, one for each day of the week, and nodded gently to Malherbes. Malherbes bent down to the drawer *Jeudi*—because it was Thursday—and took from it a salmon-coloured folder with a sulphur label, on which was written, 'Birthday Party, February 25, 1937, Mrs George Washington Kelly.'

Gabriel carried the folder up to his room, Malherbes bowed and left. In his room, Gabriel took off his fine tail-coat, which was rounded from much bowing, hung it up, sat on his bed, and carefully unfolded the bills that five-, ten-, and one-dollar patrons had pressed into his hand. He added them up and entered into a little crimson book, 'February 25, *Déjeuner*, $56'. Then he took off his boots, leaned back into the pillows, stretched his toes in the sheer, black Sulka silk socks, and opened the salmon-coloured folder.

Madame George Washington Kelly was a difficult and exacting client.

The Italian waiters called her *bestia*, the French *canaille*, and the Germans *die alte Sau*. She had a desperate countenance, partly concealed by a veil; behind this, her face shone the colour of indigo. Her skin had the texture of volcanic rock seen from the air, with dirty snow swept into the crevices.

She dressed with complete immunity to fashion, except for the Beaux Arts Ball. On the night of that elaborate *affaire* she had come with her friend, the 'Spirit of the Midnight Sun', and together they had engaged the rooms and made the preliminary plans for this birthday party, of which Malherbes had said to Gabriel in *sotto voce* French, "It is not a birthday party—it is a centennial celebration." Gabriel had stared him into silence.

After many more visits and consultations with architects, stage designers, and florists, Madame had decided to build, at one end of the ballroom, a replica of her Miami retreat, 'O Sole Mio', in its original noble dimensions. This was to be set among hibiscus, poinciana, and orange trees in bloom, surrounded by forty-foot royal palm trees and fronted by wide terraces. Cutting through the centre of the room, from the terraces on the north to a magnificent flight of stairs on the south, ran the lagoon, filled with real water, and in this water was to float the genuine gondola which Mr George Washington Kelly had brought as a souvenir from Venice and taken all the way to Miami. The stairs on the north end rose to a balcony; from there a birthday cake was to be carried down, placed on the gondola, and rowed across to Sole Mio, where Mrs Kelly's own darkies would bring it to her table to be cut.

The gondola was in Miami, also the royal palms, also the four white-haired darkies, brothers named Morandus. The

Fire Department had sent a captain to study the position of the hydrants and windows, to connect a pumping-truck, and to fill the lagoon, which it was estimated would take fourteen hours.

To do all this properly, the complete entertaining facilities of the hotel had been rented for the three days preceding the party and for an additional two following it, to clear away the débris.

Since Monday morning, the house was filled with draughts from open doors and windows, tall ladders, and empty smilax crates. Careless carpenters, careless stage-hands, careless plumbers and florists, ruined the peace and the carpets of the hotel with hammering, riveting, and soldering together the two-hundred-foot tank. Following on the heels of the plumbers came the painters, who painted the sides of the lagoon emerald green and a pattern of underwater scenery on its bottom. An eminent artist from Coral Gables supervised this.

The menu for this party was dictated by Madame herself, without benefit of Gabriel's advice. It was in the tradition of her entertainments and composed itself—at twelve dollars a cover for four hundred guests—of the following: *Caviar aux Blinis, Borsch, Homard Sole Mio, Faisan Miami, Purée de Marrons, Pommes Soufflées, Salade Georges et Marthe, Bombe Washington, Café.*

For the one thousand five hundred additional guests for supper she had chosen an equally unfortunate repast. This, at five dollars a cover, consisted of *Velouté Marthe aux Croûtons, Poussin en Cocotte Washington, Nouilles Polonaise, Petits Pois Parisienne, Bombe Sole Mio aux Fraises Cardinal, Gâteaux Georges, Café.*

Breakfast was to be served from four o'clock on, at one dollar and fifty cents per person. Provision was also made for eighty musicians' suppers, suppers for chauffeurs, maids, the secretaries at the door, and the announcer and detectives, at one dollar per person.

Cocktails were to be served during the reception: a fantastic, violent drink of Madame's own invention, named 'High Diddle', the secret formula for which Madame fortunately gave to no one. Closely guarded, her trusty darkies—the Morandi—were to mix this, bringing most of the ingredients themselves.

After Gabriel had read the papers and made several notes,

he rose, looked into a mirror, and took a loose smoking-jacket from his closet. He slipped on a pair of white gloves and walked below. Malherbes was waiting for him. It was six o'clock.

Gabriel nodded, and his assistant followed him with a silver pencil and morocco portfolio.

They walked through the kitchen, where the cooks fished red lobsters out of steaming casseroles and chopped them in half. From there they went on to the cellar—here men broke open cases of *cordon rouge* 1921, at eleven dollars a bottle, put them away in tubs, and stood them on top of one another. From here they walked up to the ballroom proper. The tables, seating eight guests each, were set to the left and right of the lagoon. Sole Mio was finished, and on the lower terraces in front of it—as indicated on the plan—was the crescent-shaped table, facing the room. Here Monsieur and Madame George Washington Kelly and their son, George Washington Kelly, Jr, as well as their most intimate friends were to sit.

Two painters were busy pouring and stirring fifty gallons of turquoise ink into the lagoon, to give it the precise colour of the waters in Miami. The Coral Gables artist had left with them a sample of that shade on a piece of water-colour paper, and, from time to time, they compared this and then added more ink. Up on the balcony of Sole Mio two electricians were focusing spot-lights across the room, up to the magenta curtain on the other side.

From the street could be heard the last '*Poooommmph*', '*Puuuuuumph*', '*Poomph*' of the Fire Department pumping-truck. The lagoon was filled.

Gabriel, walking into the halls, saw the last of twenty royal palms—in tubs, with their leaves carefully bandaged—being carried upstairs, and below from the street appeared the neck of the Venetian gondola.

The great Maître nodded to Malherbes. Malherbes ran down to the door and told the men: "Watch out for the paint, you." Later on, in the office, Malherbes made certain that a gondolier had been engaged. Yes, he had. He was to report at the ballroom in costume, with a knowledge of how to row a gondola and ability to sing '*O Sole Mio*'.

Gabriel went back to his room, lit a cigarette, and rested in his bath for half an hour. Then he dressed.

As on every evening, so now, he received the dinner guests of the hotel at the door of the restaurant.

Madame George Washington Kelly's party over in the ballroom was in the able hands of his third assistant, Monsieur Rudi, a withered, one-time stable-boy of Prince Esterházy.

At regular intervals a courier crossed from the ballroom and whispered to Malherbes, "The guests are arriving." Then again, "The cocktails are being passed." After this, "The guests are entering the ballroom." Then, "Madame George Washington Kelly is very pleased," and on to "The guests are sitting down," and "The soup is being served." These bulletins were translated into French by Malherbes and whispered on to Gabriel, who nodded.

Dinner was almost over in the restaurant when Gabriel went into a little side room, where, on a table behind a screen, a plain meal was prepared for him. It consisted of some cold pheasant, cut from the bones, field salad with lemon dressing, and a plain compôte of black cherries cooked without sugar. In ice under the table was his favourite wine, an elegant, slim bottle of Steinberger Kabinett, Preussische Staatsdomäne, 1921.

In the middle of his meal, before he had touched the wine, Gabriel arose abruptly, and quickly walked across the restaurant. Malherbes, who had eaten out in the second little room, swallowed quickly and followed him. Almost running, they crossed the entrance-hall of the ballroom and went up the staircase to the third palm.

Gabriel stopped, and beside him, as always, stopped Hector de Malherbes. The dessert had just been served, the remnants of the *Bombe Washington* were being carried from the room by the waiters, and, as set forth in the sheet of instructions, the lights were lowered.

Two heralds sounded the *Aïda* theme as a command to silence and attention.

The heavy magenta curtains sailed back, and high above the audience appeared the birthday cake. It was magnificent, of generous proportions, and truly beautiful. The masterpiece of Brillat Bonafou, *Chef Pâtissier* of the Cocofinger Palace Hotel, twice the winner of the Médaille d'Or de la Société Culinaire de Paris, Founder and President of the Institut des Chefs Pâtissiers de France. In weeks of patient, sensitive, loving labour, he had built a monument of sugar, tier upon tier, ten feet high, of raisin and almond cake. Of classic simplicity, yet covered with innumerable ornaments that depicted scenes from a happy sporting life. Up and down the sides of the cake, dozens of cherubim were busy carrying ribbons; these— bordeaux and emerald—represented the racing colours of the GWK stables.

But the most wonderful part of the wonderful cake was its top. There, complete in all details, stood a miniature replica of O Sole Mio, correct as to palms, orange trees, the lagoon, the gondola. Under the portico, an inch high, smiling hand in hand, stood Monsieur and Madame George Washington Kelly: Madame with a bouquet of roses; Monsieur with his ever-present cigar, an Hoyo de Monterrey, at the end of which was a microscopic tuft of cotton.

That was, however, not all. Over the miniature Sole Mio hovered a brace of doves. In their beaks, most artfully held, were electric wires, so arranged that flashing on and off they spelled first 'George' and then 'Martha'. 'George' in green, 'Martha' in red. Five lady midgets, dressed as the Quin-tuplets, carried the cake downstairs in the light of the amber spotlights.

The Hawaiians played 'Happy Birthday to You, Happy Birthday to You'. Everyone sang, and all eyes were moist.

The gondolier started to punt down the lagoon to receive the cake.

At that moment, with all eyes upon them, one of the Quin-tuplets, Yvonne, stepped on an olive pip, and turned her ankle. The cake trembled, swayed, and fell into the lagoon, taking the midgets with it. 'Ffsssss-hss' went the electric wires.

But where was Gabriel?

He stood under the royal palm and nodded quietly to Mal-herbes. Malherbes lifted one finger and looked up at the man with the spotlight.

The amber light left the lagoon and raced up the stairs. Out came the trumpeters again and sounded the *Aïda* theme; the curtain swung open once more, again the Hawaiians played 'Happy Birthday to You, Happy Birthday to You'.

As if the last dreadful minutes had never been on the watches of this world, there appeared to the unbelieving eyes of Monsieur and Madame George Washington Kelly and their guests and friends—THE CAKE again, unharmed, made with equal devotion, again the work of Brillat Bonafou, identically perfect and complete, with the scenes of the happy life, the cherubim, cigar and smoke, lagoon and gondola, doves, lights flashing the names in green and red, and carried on the shoulders of a new set of Quintuplets.

The miserable first set of midgets swam to the shore of the lagoon, scrambled out, and tried to leave the ballroom in the shade of the tables.

Gabriel hissed "*Imbéciles*" to Malherbes. Malherbes hissed "*Imbéciles*" down to the midgets.

The new cake was rowed across, besung, carried to the table, cut, and served. Not until then did the great Maître d'hôtel leave the protecting shadow of the royal palm. Now he walked quietly, unseen, to his room, for, in spite of possessing every talent, and besides the gift of 'Anticipation', Gabriel was a very modest man.

GRAPHIC SECTION

Gluyas Williams   The New Yorker

THE INNER MAN: Bedtime Snack

JAMES THURBER

The Beast in Me and Other Animals

The Living,
or Spitting, Image (*left*)
and a Dead Ringer

A female Volt
with all her Ergs
in one Gasket

The male
and female Tryst

The Early and the Late Riser

A TRIO OF PREHISTORIC CREATURES

Left to right: The Thesaurus, the Stereopticon and the Hexameter. The tree is a Sacroiliac

SAUL STEINBERG

The Passport

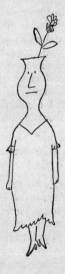

Ogden Nash

THERE ARE two different approaches to Ogden Nash, but both are fairly tortuous, and it might be better just to sit and wait for him. As he has written himself:

> What would you do if you were up a dark alley
> with Caesar Borgia
> And he was coming torgia . . .

Ogden Nash, the perpetrator of puns, of excruciating rhymes, of unending lines, is by now well known in this country, and frequently imitated, since we are a people who like puns even more than our cousins do. But there are the American critics who have traced Nash's art back not only to Walt Whitman, but also to the doggerel days of Julia Moore, the Sweet Singer of Michigan (1874–1920). Miss Moore wrote extremely bad verse without knowledge of its defects, and her subjects ranged from elegies on deaths caused by yellow fever to occasional offerings for the Cricket Club in Grand Rapids. We in this country have our broadsheet tradition too, and it may be that, adding a comparison with the verbal dexterity of W. S. Gilbert, we could produce a paper on the origins of what came to be called 'The Golden Trashery of Ogden Nashery'. One hitherto undiscovered connection in thought between Nash and Dorothy Parker would be his echo of her remark on girls who wear glasses:

> A girl who is bespectacled
> She may not get her necktacled . . .

The long, irregular line, with the startling rhyme, is probably here to stay, and it remains to be seen how long Ogden Nash will remain faithful to it. He is, as far as I am aware, its onlie begetter, but it's not a difficult style of verse to write, and may well become as popular and permanent as the clerihew.

In his own country, Ogden Nash is also known as a writer for the stage and, among his own friends, as a resourceful compiler of ballads for private parties. In S. J. Perelman's travel book *Westward Ha!* there is a sketch of Nash, drawn by Hirschfeld. This portrait, rare as a Droeshout study of a Bard, shows him to be small, neat and wearing the heavy spectacles favoured by impresarios. Altogether an engaging personality, Mr Nash, with a quick-silver wit. Now, having passed fifty, he shows signs of writing straight, sentimental poems for children. It is to be hoped he will get over this quickly, and enter his second childhood.

⬦

THE TURTLE

The turtle lives 'twixt plated decks
Which practically conceal its sex.
I think it clever of the turtle
In such a fix to be so fertile.

BIOLOGICAL REFLECTION

A girl whose cheeks are covered with paint
Has an advantage with me over one whose ain't.

OH, DID YOU GET THE TICKETS?
BECAUSE I DON'T THINK I'LL GO,
AFTER ALL

Women are more privileged than men, because if a man hasn't any muscle he can't be muscular,
But even if a woman hasn't any bustle she can still be buscular,
And women have one particular important privilege,
Which is changing their mind, which we shall call swivelage,
And I don't know the exact percentage of it,
But I should say that in about ninety-five out of every hundred decisions they take advantage of it;
Indeed, just as you might say that if you don't discard a green persimmon in favour of a ripe one you are making a persimmon error,

E   129

Why, women feel that their first decision is simply a pre-
liminerror,

But the path by which they arrive at their final decision is a
devious one,

And somehow they never communicate their final decision to
you until you have acted irrevocably on their previous one,

Because some women may go so far as to treat some men
leniently,

But never to the extent of changing their mind helpfully if they
can change it inconveniently.

Just as it really begins to rain they announce that what they
would simply adore is gumdrops, and you mention the rain,
and they give you a look that implies that your spine is
spaghetti and your soul is lard,

So you say you will go get the gumdrops and they thank you
sweetly and say for heaven's sake don't get the squashy
kind, get them good and hard,

So you go out and you have to go to three places before you
can unearth the hard kind, and you return dripping and
hand the box over and they gaze at you with dreamy eyes as
if they had just been gazing on some angelic vision aloft,

And they say they are so sorry but right after you went out
they remembered that a fortuneteller told them hard gumdrops were unlucky, would you mind exchanging these for
soft?

And sometimes they get you to go to an auction and overbid
extravagantly for a clock of ormolu,

And if you protest they say " 'Oo doesn't know anysing about
art, 'oo dreat big darlin' subnormal 'oo."

And an hour later they say, "That clock wasn't the right shape
for the mantelpiece, was it?"

So they ask you to calmly go back and calmly ask the auction-
eer to return your deposit.

Oh, a boy's will is the wind's will, if we are to believe the poet,

But a girl's will is a won't, but not until it doesn't do you any
good to know it.

Candy
Is dandy
But liquor
Is quicker.

HOME, 99 44/100% SWEET HOME

Most of the time, oh most of the time,
I like to sit at home,
With a good fire, and a good chair,
And a good detective tome.
What can a man, can a family man
Ask in the way of cheer
More than a pipe, and a reading lamp,
And a modest mug of beer?
Most of the time, the wealth of the Indies
Wouldn't tempt me to blowouts or shindies.

But once in a while,
Oh, once in a while,
It's pleasant to paint the town,
To frolic and revel,
A regular devil,
And do the evening brown,
To buy an orchid, or maybe two,
And woo the way that you used to woo,
To press the loot from the babies' banks
On waiters who fail to murmur thanks,
To dine and wine and dance and sup,
And ride in a cab till the sun comes up,
And to feel thereafter, in sundry ways,
Simply awful for days and days.
Home is heaven and orgies are vile,
But I like an orgy, once in a while.

Home is the place, oh home is the place
That no place else is like,

131

So who would freeze in the South, like Byrd,
Or discover peaks, like Pike?
Who so animal, who so low
As to pant for the Great White Way?
Who would give up a night at home
For one in a cabaret?
Most of the time I'd swim to Australia
As soon as engage in a Saturnalia.

But once in a while,
Oh, once in a while,
It's pleasant to loop the loop,
To daringly seize
The flying trapeze
With a cry of Allez-oop!
To jump the rails, kick over the traces,
To go on the town and visit places,
Sit ten at a table meant for two,
And choke on smoke as you used to do,
To tread the floor with the dancing bears,
They on your feet, and you on theirs,
To have flings at things that philosophers true shun,
And undermine your constitue-shun,
Home is heaven and orgies are vile,
But you need an orgy, once in a while.

Cornelia Otis Skinner
and Emily Kimbrough

IN THE 'twenties and 'thirties the traditional pilgrimage of writer and composer was from New York to Paris. Here Elliot Paul lived in his Narrow Street, here Gershwin reflected the jaunty step of the American on the boulevard, here Cole Porter was known as Colporteur, and Robert Benchley struggled with the language, and here the hearts of Miss Otis Skinner and Miss Kimbrough were young and gay.

These two enterprising ladies—and 'enterprising' is the exact phrase for Americans abroad—also discovered London. But London has surely never made an American visitor feel young or gay. We produce in our younger cousins a blend of sentiment, respect, and pity, a kind of autumnal affection shot with only an occasional burst of merriment.

If forced to a definition, I would be willing to classify the Skinner–Kimbrough approach as extrovert humour. It is as buoyant and sustaining as the chatter of the American girls one meets on boat-trains and in airport lounges. Miss Otis Skinner, after this first joint description of her escapades, went on alone as a family chronicler and humorist, still displaying the artlessness which conceals the art—the sort of personal revelation which condenses so well into the pages of the *Readers Digest*. Miss Kimbrough, not to be outdone, has written her own family reminiscences, centred in Virginia. It seems that the hearts of Otis Skinner and Kimbrough, though no longer quite so young, are (in the phrase of Mehitabel the Cat to Archy) *toujours gai*.

❖

OUR HEARTS WERE YOUNG AND GAY

Paul White stayed on in Southampton for a few days. When I think not only of his generosity in sacrificing so much of his holiday time, but of his saving me from that fate worse than death, the German quarantine camp, I am his for life at any time he ever wants me (Dr White of Boston please note). He made certain my rash had come forth as it should and that despite the risk involved in landing with a temperature of 102° I was not going to have pneumonia. Then he went on his way while the rest of us stayed on in that terminal hotel for ten mortal days and nights. Those ten days passed by only because days eventually do. The wearisome passage of time meant less to me than to the others. I just lay in an aching doze scarcely aware of what was going on around me. As a matter of fact, what was going on around me was no great shakes, for Emily, at any rate. Mother at least was kept busy nursing me, and Father didn't especially mind this enforced halt in their travel itinerary, as it gave him a chance to work on the script of next season's play. But poor Emily! Her introduction to Europe, that Europe over which she had cried with such tender appreciation, was anything but colourful. She had pictured her first night on English soil taking place in some quiet wayside inn, peaceful, quaint, and of course thatched, where in a Jacobean bed in a dear little chintz-trimmed room she would drift off to sleep lulled by the tinkle of sheep-bells and the scent of hedgerows. Instead she found herself in a room which was in some way suspended out over the railroad tracks. What held it up was a mystery, unless possibly it rested on the bridge of a signal tower. Trains passed to and fro directly under the floor. She could open her window and get a bird's-eye view of a locomotive, to say nothing of some deep drafts of Welsh coal smoke. Engines puffed and shunted beneath her bed all night long, and when from sheer exhaustion she'd be dropping off to sleep, her ears and nerves would be suddenly shattered by the hysterical screech of a British whistle, which sounds like the whoop of an elderly spinster who has suddenly been pinched. If her nights were wakeful, her days were dreary dull. She'd wander down to the docks and gaze at the ocean liners, but even Cunarders can pall in interest after a while. Then she'd amble dolefully back to the terminal hotel for one of those meals which is to be had, thank God, only in terminal hotels. Too much has already been said and written by sassy Americans on the subject of the English commercial cuisine. Suffice it to say that Emily didn't like it either.

After a day or so, when he saw that his child in all probability wasn't going to die, Father eased the tedium of things for Emily by taking her on a few day trips, the New Forest, Winchester and such, which was a good thing from all points of view. Heretofore Emily had been pretty much awed and even a little terrified of Father. He in turn had regarded her as he regarded all my playmates, as creatures to be at once treated politely, and avoided as much as possible. Now, however, they became close and giddy buddies, a fact that filled me with that special and fatuous sort of pride you feel when your favourite people hit it off well, as if you'd done it all yourself. Emily's awe of Father vanished into thin air, and when she was with him she relaxed her efforts at being sophisticated, and became less a *femme fatale* than a giggling school-girl. And Father found Emily slightly mad, constantly amusing, and like no one he'd ever met before. They'd return from an outing in a state of hilarity. One could hear them coming from way down the length of the corridor. Father on entering my room would call out in clarion tones, "Where's my measly child?" or "How's the Spotted Peril?" and have to be frantically shushed by Mother.

The *Empress* stayed in port three days before going on to Hamburg. We had one *mauvais quart d'heure* when the ship's doctor, who possibly had had his suspicions all along, took it upon himself to send up his card saying he'd heard I'd been suffering from a slight cold and could he see me. I remembered the doctor as being aloof and impassive, like a forbidding version of C. Aubrey Smith. The prospect of undergoing his penetrating stare shot my temperature up. It was certain they'd found out about me. I recalled the rigid British quarantine laws regarding dogs, and began to think that maybe they applied to infected human beings as well, in which event I'd be held for six months in some place like Spratt's kennels, where my loved ones could visit me only on Sundays. But I was reckoning without Mother and her gentle wiles. She put on her prettiest hat, and with a radiant smile tripped down to greet the doctor and tell him all about her daughter . . . well, perhaps not quite all. A half hour later Emily and Father came upon them having tea amid the potted palms and engines. The doctor was asking if he might show her about Southampton, that is, if her husband would trust her to an old dog like him—ha-ha!—an old sea-dog—ha-ha-ha!

In time my temperature subsided to normal, my rash faded away, and none of those adult complications of a pulmonary or mastoid nature developed. In a week I was on my feet again, not that my feet were particularly good, but heaven knows my knees weren't any. But I flopped about, gradually gaining strength, and after three days of sunshine and Bovril was sufficiently recovered for us all to depart for London in that open Daimler. Mother bundled me up so I could hardly breathe, and I don't remember being able to see at all. I was swaddled in mufflers and sweaters, and I had the further discomfort of being forced to wear Emily's appalling Canadian greatcoat. I still felt awful and I think I must have looked awful too. But I struck a disgustingly gallant attitude, rather fancying myself an Elizabeth Barrett who was not long for this world. We stopped off at a number of points of interest and culture, most of which made little or no impression on me. I'm the uncivilized type who doesn't take in things unless I'm healthy. I do remember remaining overnight at Salisbury. Emily and my parents wandered diligently about the cathedral while I slumped on a seat in a posture of meditation trying to think about Gothic architecture but in reality brooding about whether it would be consumption or melancholia which would carry me off.

I felt better next morning. It was market day and the sight of those rosy-cheeked, smocked farmers who might have stepped out of a bright Moreland print, the thick fat sheep, and the glorious thundering Clydesdales, their hooves heavy with umbrellas of hair, manes gay with straw and ribbon plaitings, and the biggest, roundest, most beautiful rumps in the entire animal kingdom, exuded an aura of health, and I found myself perking up and deciding I might, after all, last out the summer.

We visited the cemetery at Stoke Poges and took snapshots of each other sitting with gingerly reverence on the tombstone of Thomas Gray. And we stopped off to see Stonehenge, and to have a picnic lunch amid those great inexplicable slabs which Emily kept calling 'troglodytes', a name which strikes me as being as fitting for them as any other. The weather had been that average English June weather, which for the most part is terrible. It rained a lot, and the inns at which we stayed were dank and wintry and guiltless of any heat because people went on the theory that after all it was June and one didn't have heating in June, and if the weather chose to be beastly the only thing to do was pay no attention to it. I shook with constant chills, and Emily said she knew she was coming down with ague; she wasn't certain just what ague was but it sounded like something that would be a logical result of British weather. However, there were times when our discomfort would vanish like a bad dream; those were the times when the sun came out the way it does only in England. When one had reached the conclusion that it's the most wretched country on the globe the sun comes out just long enough to prove that it's the most beautiful. The car sped along in that giddy left-handed manner which makes you feel you must tap the chauffeur on the shoulder and say, "Over to the right, my good man," past hedgerows shining with recent rain, and maytrees festive with bloom. One could hear the sweet, shrill music of larks, and we tried quoting 'Hail to thee, blithe spirit', but couldn't get beyond 'and soaring ever singest'. Still we felt we were pretty intellectual and so did Mother; that is, she thought it was a step in the right direction. Houses became closer together, and the outline of London hove into sight. Again we tried to quote something, but I could only think of 'Westminster Bridge' and Emily kept muttering "Childe Roland to the dark tower came," to which Father rudely appended "His cohorts were gleaming with purple and gold." After which, Mother said she thought we'd better stop trying.

Once arrived in London, we parted company with Mother and Father. They had served their purpose during my illness. Now I was recovered and 'raring' to be independent again. They went their way (I daresay somewhat secretly relieved, if truth were told) to their habitual caravansary, the Hotel Victoria in Northumberland Avenue, while Emily and I set forth for the more bohemian atmosphere of 'lodgings'. Through some colourful flight of fancy we had made arrangements to take over the rooms of a former Bryn Mawr student who had spent the previous winter working for a PhD at the University of London. She was one of these brilliant scholars far too intellectual to be concerned with creature comforts, and after we saw the way she lived we came to the conclusion that we weren't intellectual types after all. She had written us that she was leaving for a 'hiking' trip (that fine outdoor term implicit of any number of splendid things in the way of blisters, fish and chips, and a brave avoidance of baths). However, she assured us that the landlady was fully cognizant of our arrival, and would be waiting for us with welcome at I forget what number Tavistock Square. As a cheery afterthought she added she hoped we'd be happy in her 'digs', a word which slightly startled us and made us wonder if we were to lodge in some sort of cellar.

The 'digs', however, proved to be on the topmost floor of an ancient manse which had been converted into a rooming house along about the beginning of the reign of Edward VII. It was situated in a part of London neither chic nor quaint, an extremely commonplace district somewhere back of the British Museum, and from the glimpses we caught of the other lodgers, it looked as if they'd come straight out of some of the cases. One toiled up four flights of extremely audible stairs and collapsed into our quarters consisting of two dreary, barren rooms which, when the residence had known better days, must have housed the tweenie and the second footman. One contained a bed, a studio couch, and a washstand with an assortment of bowls, pitchers, and soap dishes which didn't match, being for the most part souvenirs from Brighton and the Exhibition of 1854. We gathered this must be the bedroom and through the process of elimination came to the ingenious conclusion that the other was a sitting-room, although it looked more like a semi-denuded storeroom. It contained a desk which had been made out of a grand piano, a couple of Morris chairs fancied up with antimacassars, a small fireplace with a coal grate, and a framed picture of Watts' 'Hope', that dejected symbol of anything but. There was also a bookcase containing on the top shelf the Bryn Mawr scholar's textbooks, which were so erudite we couldn't understand their titles, and on the lower shelf a brass alcohol lamp and a teapot shaped like a duck or some such whimsey. The landlady had gone off for a holiday up the Thames and we were left to the tender mercies of a Cockney slavey. She'd clatter in at seven am to fix the one fire we had all day, then at seven-thirty she'd charge back with a pitcher of hot water, which in London June weather didn't stay hot very long. At eight she'd bring us a tasty breakfast: half an orange for each, fried eggs and leathery bacon, a pot of that witch's brew they call coffee, and some slabs of toast arranged in an open-air rack to insure their being nice and cold. When we petitioned ever so meekly permission to receive these blessings a trifle later in the day, she said, "Carn't, Miss. Mrs 'Iggins horders." Some mornings we'd say to hell with Mrs Higgins and breakfast, and turn over for a couple of hours' more sleep; but during such periods of oblivion the water would have become the glacial temperature of the room, and the fire would have gone out. Starting the fire required a knack known only to the slavey, who miraculously got those bits of damp kindling and chunks of igneous rock ignited by spreading a newspaper across the fireplace and blowing vociferously. We'd try that, too, but the only thing to ignite would be the newspaper, and one of us would have to come running with a water pitcher to put out the conflagration, not that a conflagration could have made much headway in that room. This commotion would arouse the slavey, who would poke her face in the doorway and say severely that Mrs 'Iggins wouldn't 'arf be put out, which was her simple homespun way of implying that if we persisted in such tricks we'd be the ones who'd be put out.

The bathroom was down two flights of stairs, and that involved some interesting encounters with the other tenants, all of whom seemed to be elderly gentlemen in conservative bathrobes, carrying towels, shaving mugs, and copies of the *Daily Mail*. Emily nearly knocked one down the stairs one morning, and to hide her confusion spoke to him in her most friendly Indiana way. But he gave her the disdainful look he must in his younger days have cast at a Piccadilly *fille de joie* and shot for sanctuary through the nearest door.

The first morning in this giddy establishment Emily, who had been holding converse with the slavey, said to me, "There's some queer sort of character who lives in this house."

"Queer?"

"Yes," she said, "that girl just told me. He's apparently some sort of old eccentric, and when you see him you have to tip him.

"She said, 'You'll have to look out for the geezer, Miss. It's always best to have tuppence handy for the geezer.'"

I felt this to be another of Emily's original flights of fancy, but what it meant didn't dawn on me until I went down for my bath. The water for the tub was heated by one of those little gas-jet arrangements which flicker beneath a small copper boiler. After a time, if you're lucky, a forlorn trickle of hot water dribbles forth, cooling off considerably before it hits the tin tub below. I remembered this was called a geyser and went back upstairs to tell Emily so. She became indignant, as she always does when she's misunderstood a thing.

"Then why don't they call it a geyser?" she snapped.

"They do. Only they pronounce it geezer."

"I suppose they call Old Faithful a water-pistol!"

The geezer was a mercenary contraption. There was a slot into which one dropped two coppers to pay for the gas. When twopence worth was consumed the gas went out. We were informed that if this occurred when we were still running the water we must immediately insert two more coins in the slot. If we didn't, the slavey prophesied, "everythink might blow hup". I well remember one morning when, as I was disporting myself like a dolphin in a couple of inches of tepid water, the gas gave a blue spurt, and with a little dying hiccough went out completely. The room was of that bracing June chill and I hadn't even started soaping myself. I yelled to Emily to bring me some more coins. She didn't have any coppers in her purse, but she came down the stairs two at a time with a six-pence. All this accomplished was merely to drop down the slot and on to the floor without in any way rousing the gas. I recalled the slavey's warning about the thing blowing up unless, like Mammon, you kept it stoked with coins. Odd rumblings were issuing from the little copper boiler. Emily, always active, if not always logical in an emergency, cried, "Don't move, darling!" and pushed me back into the chilly water. She dashed downstairs, but couldn't find a living soul. The slavey had vanished, and those elderly gentlemen, the other lodgers, had either gone to business or were hiding behind locked doors. She stepped out on to the street in search of a shop or even a flower vendor who might make change. But Tavistock Square is guiltless of any shops. They haven't a news-stand. Then a bus pulled up beside her, and that seemed to solve the problem. Hatless and coatless, she jumped on the back platform, got changed for two and six, rode one block, and jumped off, murmuring to the bewildered conductor, "You see, my friend is up there stark naked with the geezer and I have to hurry back to her," which straightened everything out nicely. By the time she returned I had turned quite blue with cold, but Old Faithful had not yet erupted.

For all that little financial lesson in the Montreal Hotel, Emily was still confused by British currency. She'd grown highly incensed not only with it but with me because she couldn't understand it. (It was the only thing I ever heard her admit to not understanding.) It was in vain that I tried to show her the difference between a half crown and a two shilling piece. She refused to admit they were anything but two versions of fifty cents and persisted in being so stubbornly obtuse about it I finally told her if she'd just bring herself to read what was written on them she'd know. This didn't work out so well either, because she'd keep taxi drivers waiting interminably while she'd scan the reading matter of each and every coin, turning it round and round, sometimes breathing on it and rubbing it clear. When I suggested that people might think her awfully queer she said not at all, they'd merely mistake her for a coin collector. I tried explaining that 'one florin' meant two shillings, but that only made her madder. The day we received a bill made out in guineas, and I told her that there was no such thing as a guinea, it was a pound and one shilling, only the swanker shops charged you in guineas, and you paid in pounds and shillings, but you called it guineas although, as I had said, there really was no such thing, she slapped me.

That was the summer when white fur evening wraps were the rage. One saw them everywhere. They ranged from chic models of dazzling ermine to cheap copies in rabbit. Some of the cheaper ones weren't too bad, or maybe they were bad, all right, but a few smart women wore them, and to us they spelled enchantment. The only fur coat I'd ever had was made of what the salesgirl had vowed was 'mountain lion' but what wore into a substance more like circus lion, and a retired one at that, while Emily's was a cutdown squirrel of her mother's. As for evening wraps, the best I could boast was a tasty mandarin jacket, while Emily still clung to the green velvet cloak Grandmother Kimbrough had brought her from the San Francisco Exposition. We felt that if ever the day arrived when we could afford white fur evening wraps we'd believe in fairy godmothers. Then suddenly the day arrived when we found we could. Emily out for a solitary stroll one morning had spied a shop whose window displayed a vision of rabbit splendour marked £6 10s. 6d. She had a feeling this was within our humble means, but not being quite certain, she rushed back to our dovecote to ask me what 'El six, ten esses and six dees' meant. With the then rate of exchange it was about the equivalent of $30. We lost no time, rushed to the shop, and without a moment's hesitation bought a couple, one each, and exactly alike. That was the incredible era of shapeless dresses and shapeless wrap-around coats with voluminous sleeves and rolled collars. Our models were capes, and as I recall them now they must have been daisy-bells. Made of snowy rabbit (we were later to discover it was not only white but flying), they were fashioned along the lines of a tent, adorned with a deep yoke and an even deeper object known as a 'cape collar'. They were perfectly enormous and we could wrap them about us twice with a d'Artagnan flourish which we thought was chic and gave us a worldly air. Not daring to entrust these treasures to a delivery boy, we ourselves lugged them in huge boxes back to our lodgings, where we spent a lot of time parading in them before a large and pallid mirror hanging above the washstand.

That evening Mother and Father asked us to dinner. The family, with supreme tact, always made a great point of asking us to dine with them, never letting on that they knew we'd leap at the chance. It was their indulgent way of co-operating with us in that fine independence we talked so much about. When they didn't, we felt forlorn and went to places like Lyons or the ABC, where we felt even more forlorn. Some evenings, because it was inexpensive and near our lodgings, we ate at a dreadful temperance hotel. The food was tasteless, the napkins grey and damp as the people, and we'd emerge dyspeptic and full of gloom. We longed to, but never dared, venture into any place as worldly as a restaurant, even a modest Soho café, because we were too shy. This particular evening we were invited to dine at the Trocadero, a dizzy prospect. What better occasion than this, we thought, for the world *première* of those fur coats? After the novelty of trying them on had abated somewhat, we began to feel a slight uneasiness as to just how we'd break the news of their purchase to Mother. She was apt to grow severe over any undue extravagance, particularly abroad, where, according to her standards, it was all right to spend money on culture, but to squander it on clothes came under the heading of original sin. However, we felt confident that our entrance into the restaurant would forestall any objections. We'd be so breathtakingly beautiful to behold, she'd be rendered speechless. Well, she was.

We dressed with care, arraying ourselves in our best evening dress. Anything less fine would hardly have been worthy of the occasion. It so happened that we also dressed exactly alike because our best evening get-up were bridesmaids' dresses we had worn at a friend's wedding, and so expensive we hadn't been able to buy any others since. Then, wrapping the great bell-shaped cloaks about us, we set forth from the lodging-house feeling like personifications of Queen Marie of Roumania and Peggy Hopkins Joyce. We had to walk a block or two before we found a taxi. It was one of those evenings characteristic of the London season, when one goes out to dinner in broad daylight. People stared at us somewhat, but we didn't mind. We thought it was because we looked so dazzling. We may have looked dazzling, but we also looked like a pair of igloos out for a stroll. We spied a taxi, hailed it, and gave with a good deal of grandeur the address of the Trocadero. As we clambered in I rather received the impression that the driver said, "Right you are, Snowball," but decided I must be mistaken. Fearful of harming our new and spotless purchases by sitting on them, we pulled them out from under us, and held them up gingerly about our midriffs and shoulders. The things rose in the breeze and billowed out, filling all available space. We were pretty well snowed under. The taxi came to a stop before the Trocadero, and laboriously we began working our way out of the fur clouds. Getting out of a taxi is not one of life's nimbler activities under the easiest of conditions, but to get out when weighted down by a white fur pup-tent was a feat indeed. We emerged in jackknife posture, managed to make the pavement on our feet and not our foreheads, shook ourselves out, and paid the cabman, who was grinning broadly in what we never doubted was admiration. Then I caught sight of Father. He was waiting for us outside the restaurant. But for some curious reason he was leaning against the wall, and for an even more curious reason tears were running down his face. He looked to be hysterical. I couldn't imagine what was the matter. Emily, who didn't know him so well, thought that he must be in the throes of some unfathomable mood inherent in a great actor, and that whatever might be causing it, the radiant vision of the two of us would bring him out of it pretty quick. We smiled at him and waved graciously the way we thought Mary Garden might. At this, he covered his face with a handkerchief and shook as if he were in the throes of some sort of malarial chill. We looked at one another with blank amazement and Emily hissed, "What's making him take on so?" It never remotely entered our vaguest suspicions that we might have something to do with it. We approached him shyly and were about to inquire softly if there were anything we might do, when he looked out from behind the handkerchief and we realized his tears were due to wild, uncontrollable laughter.

"Oh, my God!" he managed to choke forth. "How could you get so *many* rabbits!" We couldn't believe our ears. "And what," he went on, "in the name of dear, sweet gentle heaven was that can-can movement you were doing in the taxi with your skirts up over your heads?"

I was deeply offended and said "*Father!*" in a crushing tone, but he continued being anything but crushed. He led the way into the restaurant, and we followed, still trying to look like Mary Garden, but with an uncomfortable hunch that maybe what we most closely resembled were Flopsy and Mopsy in *Peter Rabbit*. Mother had seen our entrance, and by the time we reached the table she was in a condition of hysteria similar to Father's. We were hurt and quite bewildered. The only consoling thing was the fact that Mother was too weak to become cross over my extravagance, and she did agree that it was a great deal of fur for $30.

They treated us to champagne that evening, which did a lot to soothe our wounded pride. And as a further aid to reestablishing our self-confidence, Father ordered some especially old Courvoisier. Emily at the sight of the large brandyglass said, "Mercy! I won't be able to drink that big a glassful!" She could never forget her great-grandmother Curry, who shortly after the Civil War had pulled off a spectacular buggy-ride in record time to open the first prohibition campaign in Ohio. She was relieved but also somewhat disappointed when the wine captain poured out a dab which barely covered the bottom. That dab had its effect, however, for after sipping and sniffing it for a time she said she guessed she'd had enough because the room was starting to go round. Father said that was all right, when it came time for us to go home all she'd have to do would be to go across to Trafalgar Square, sit on one of the lions and wait till Tavistock Square came round.

We spent our time sight-seeing, buying dozens of postcards we never sent, and sponging off the family as many free meals as possible. Life was pleasant and would have been perfect had we not been obliged to start and end up each day in that doleful lodging-house. To be sure, we were being independent, but we began to think that as far as creature comforts were concerned, independence wasn't so hot (and when I remember the temperature of those rooms the word is apt). The family suggested ever so delicately that we might like to change to their hotel, and we leapt at the chance like hungry trout to a succulent fly. We moved into a small but comfortable room near them, and once securely no longer on our own, began again to feel *mondaine*. We dressed for dinner every night, which set us up all right. Occasionally Mother and Father blew us to the theatre. We'd wear our white fur coats, the shock of which had worn off by now, and try to appear *blasé*, and if ever we encountered people we knew, which was likely, as half of America was over there that summer, we'd come out with offensive remarks to the effect that there was nothing like London during the season, was there? Father took us on a few tours about town, showing us places he'd known and loved when he'd played there thirty years before with the Daly Company. He was especially fond of an old cemetery for actors. It was in a shoddy out-of-the-way district and the ground was unhallowed. Even in death, members of the profession were ostracized, because until well after the Restoration they were legally considered 'Rogues and Vagabonds', not fit to lie with gentle folk. That pleased him highly. It was evident he felt it a sorry day when players turned respectable. One day Mother, who had read in *The Times* that the Royal Family was to leave for the country at eleven, scuttled us off to Buckingham Palace to watch the departure. We stood along with a handful of governesses and casual passers-by—nobody else seemed to have made an occasion of it—when the gates opened and the Family appeared, rather crowded into one car like any other family starting for the station. The few men round us took off their hats, and the nannies pointed out the car to the children and Emily and I just looked. But not Mother. Not for nothing had she assisted on the stage the entrance of Kings and Queens. She fluttered to the ground in a deep, eighteenth-century curtsy, spreading as wide as possible the skirt of her tailored suit. We looked at her in amazement. We weren't the only ones amazed—Queen Mary nearly fell out of the car.

The family received a constant stream of callers and whenever we thought them sufficiently well known we'd horn in if possible. One afternoon Sybil Thorndike was to come to tea, also Gilbert Miller. The prospect of meeting Gilbert Miller made me rather twittery. I was about to launch forth upon the stage, and who knew, Mr Miller might offer me a job if I made an impression on him. It seemed a golden opportunity. They arrived and their visit passed pleasantly. Also a decided impression was made on Mr Miller, but not by me. My thunder was stolen by Emily, who in her excitement over this distinguished occasion ate the pink baby-ribbon which was tied around the sandwiches. It was hard to chew and even harder to swallow because it got untied in transit and she had to gulp it down like a stomach-pump. But to pull it out hand over hand would have been even more spectacular, so she washed it down with tea, hoping it wouldn't start tying itself in bowknots around her appendix. Gilbert Miller never took his eyes off her. He never even blinked. And as for topping that impression, I hadn't a chance.

Will Cuppy

"THERE," says one of Thurber's dogs, pointing a limp paw at a human family draggling across the park, "go the most intelligent of the animals!" But the fact that man has reached such a position in the evolutionary scale is not taken for granted by American humorists, who like to contemplate the lower creatures with affection, even with envy.

The modern Fable and the modern Bestiary are the most popular forms which this guilt-complex takes. Don't love me, love my dogs, may be Thurber's motto. But Will Cuppy, almost the Grand Old Man of American humour, takes a more refreshing view. He will even have us believe that some animals and birds are actually as stupid as we are, and that others —notably the Wombat—are remarkably obscure. He has been pursuing this mild and agreeable task for twenty years, and to a man who asked him, "Are you still writing those little pieces about animals?" he tells us his reply was, "Yes, I am still writing little pieces about animals. I am a person who writes little pieces about animals, I am in that business. That is what I do. See?"

Fair enough, but that is not entirely what Will Cuppy has done. In his most celebrated book, *How to Tell Your Friends from the Apes*, he did consider, for a while, the History of Man, from the Piltdown Man to the Modern Man, or Nervous Wreck, the highest of all Mammals.

Cuppy can at least look at his animals and birds objectively, without becoming involved. It was said of Benchley that when, at college, he was asked to write a term thesis on the Newfoundland Fisheries Case, his interpretation, though scholarly, was written entirely from the point of view of one of the fishes. And, to hark or bark back to Thurber, 'the claw of the sea-puss gets us all in the end'.

Being as sound in mind and body as I am ever likely to be, I have decided to release my notes on fly-swatting made from time to time during many years of active service at my Long Island beach cottage, Chez Cuppy. (It's the same old place I used to call Tobacco Road, but I think the new name sort of lends a tone—and, besides, it's a change.) In the belief that fly-swatting is here to stay for awhile, DDT and other squirts to the contrary notwithstanding, I am passing on the torch in Ten Easy Lessons, as follows:

1. Get set. Be sure you're not going to fall off your chair backwards in the act of swatting. Here as elsewhere, style is everything.

2. Still, don't take too much time with the preliminaries. The fly won't wait there forever. He has other things to do with his time.

3. Try to ascertain in some unobtrusive way whether the object you're after is actually a fly or a nail-head. Don't go poking at the thing to see which it is. When in doubt, swat.

Little situations like this are bound to occur in every swatter's routine. For instance, there is a small black spot on the ceiling of my bedroom that has embarrassed me dozens of times, it looks so exactly like a fly of some large and vicious species. If I have crept up on it once—Oh, well! Stalking an imperfection in the paint and swinging one's heart out at a nail-head are not things one likes to remember, but perhaps they have their place in the give and take of daily living. We can't be heroes to ourselves every instant.

4. In any case, never flirt your swatter back and forth past a fly before swatting, expecting to get him your next time around. When you finally make up your mind to hit him, he will not be there. The fly who hesitates is lost. He knows this and acts accordingly.

5. Take aim quickly but carefully. A complete miss is not good for the morale, either yours or the fly's.

6. If possible, fix him with the first swat. Failure to do so may be serious. For one thing, you didn't get him. That alone is bad. Secondly, conditions will never be quite the same again, since you are now dealing with an alert and disillusioned fly. He is never going to trust you as he did before. He will avoid you in future.

That was one of the many faults of my dear Aunt Etta's swatting. She never hit her fly the first time and she seldom came anywhere near him on repeated attempts, partly because she employed that worst of all swatting techniques, the folded newspaper, or slow-motion, method. She would lunge at the fly again and yet again with her antiquated weapon in a free-for-all that left her exhausted and the fly in the best of health and spirits. A folded newspaper is only about 17 per cent efficient in anybody's hands, and Aunt Etta's form was nothing to boast of. Her batting average must have been something incredible. I'm glad to state that she often thought she had won. Her eyesight wasn't so good, either.

I assure you that Aunt Etta was one of the kindest persons I have ever known, though not so soft about flies as my Uncle Toby, who did so much in his day to encourage the spread of typhoid fever and other diseases. There was certainly no sadistic urge in her swatting activities. She never engaged a fly in hand-to-hand combat until after she and we children had staged a ceremonious fly-drive with kitchen aprons and dish towels, then a second and often a third to chase the last one out the open screen door. It was only the fly or flies who failed to respect these rites that she tackled, and it always amazed me that there would be any such. If we thought Aunt Etta had one of her headaches, or felt a nap coming on, or couldn't stand such a racket—in which case she would tell us so in no uncertain terms—we disappeared. We vanished utterly, with the usual gift of cookies. But flies are not brought up that way, apparently. They cannot take a hint.

The family would want me to add that Aunt Etta's house was no more fly-ridden than any other home of the period. In fact, it was less so than most, as it was thoroughly screened. Which reminds me that she never did, to my knowledge, solve the riddle of how they got in. She was always saying there wasn't a crack where they could squeeze through. All right, then, how did the mouse get in?

7. Don't mind a little incidental breakage around the house. Aunt Etta was much too careful of her bric-à-brac. She wouldn't strike within yards of her whatnot when a fly took sanctuary there. For the cause I would smash anything in Chez Cuppy to smithereens, except possibly my shaving mirror. I'm not having seven years of bad luck for any fly.

8. Cultivate patience. It is a beautiful thing in itself, and when you are after a fly who will not light, you will need it. Eventually that fly will light, and ten to one it will be in some dark inaccessible corner, down behind the stove.

The fly who absolutely refuses to settle is a problem for advanced swatters, and not an easy one. Talk about a watched pot! Do not stalk such a fly too openly, but try to act as though you were interested in something else altogether. This involves looking wall-eyed at the fly while gazing fixedly in the other direction, but it can be done, with practice. It is my opinion that a fly will not settle while you are looking straight at him with a swatter in your fist. At any rate, he won't while you are following him around the room, making passes at him. Believe me, he knows what you are up to.

I would not go so far as to say that a fly knows the exact moment when you start looking for a swatter, if you should be caught without one. Edge yourself ever so casually in the general direction of a swatter, and notice what happens. Other persons who may be present will simply wonder why you are hitching your chair along in that insane fashion or tiptoeing across the room with one groping hand outstretched and a haunted look in your eyes. They won't have the faintest notions of what goes on, but the fly will. He has already figured out his first five moves and several of yours.

This does not necessarily prove that the fly is more intelligent than you are. If such things could be measured—and they will be, some day—I have little doubt that you, gentle swatter, would be found to have a higher IQ than the average fly. You may be slow on the uptake, while the fly is unbelievably fast. His sheer brilliance in planning and executing

manœuvres of every sort on the ground and in the air amounts to genius, and you have all you can do to keep from falling over your feet. You cannot make quick decisions, or, if you do, you are generally dead wrong, as everybody at the office knows but yourself. The fly's decisions are mostly right. They have to be.

Yet on the whole, taking it by and large, and allowing for individual exceptions, you are smarter than the fly. You know more than he does about more things. Above all, you possess the power of abstract reasoning, a faculty which distinguishes mankind from the merely brute creation, such as flies. You can listen to the radio, look at television, and go to the movies. You can read mystery stories and try to guess who done it. Keep your chin up and always remember that if you are not the fly's superior in every single respect one might mention, you are at least his equal, mentally. Since you are fighting on practically even terms, then, when you are after a fly who will not light you must seek for a flaw in his intellectual equipment if you hope to regain the initiative, and I can help you there. The key is his imperfect memory. You can remember as far back as yesterday. The fly cannot. He forgets. The particular fly of whom we are speaking will be out of his dark corner in a few brief moments, and you can begin the whole show all over again.

9. Check up on yourself occasionally. Ask yourself, 'Am I a better swatter than I was last year?' The correct answer is No.

10. Don't be discouraged at a few failures. I don't always get them myself, but I give them pause. It makes 'em think.

Wolcott Gibbs

SELF-EFFACING, content to leave his reputation secure on the dramatic criticism pages of the *New Yorker*, Wolcott Gibbs has also developed a pleasant line in parody.

The following example is a tilt at William Saroyan (but other notable victims have been Ernest Hemingway and Henry Luce of *Time* and *Life*). I wanted to include Saroyan (originator of what he calls the 'jump-in-the-river-and-start-to-swim-immediately' type of writing) in this anthology, for he sometimes laughs as he swims. But I could not find a complete Saroyan which fitted the bill. Along comes this parody by Mr Gibbs, and enables me to present two entertaining writers for the price of one.

SHAKESPEARE, HERE'S YOUR HAT

(A New Play by Mr William Saroyan, in Book Form with the Customary Prefatory Notes by the Author)

I

This play is a masterpiece. It is young, gusty, comical, tragic, beautiful, heroic, and as real as a slaughterhouse or some dame fixing her hair. It could only have been written in America, by an American boy who is an artist and a lover and a dreamer. All at once. All mixed up. It could only have been written by Saroyan.

Other people write plays, but they are no good. I go to them and I sit there and think, 'My god, this is lousy! It was written by a man in an English suit of clothes who makes fifty thousand dollars a year, but it is not alive. It is dead. It stinks.' A man making fifty thousand dollars a year doesn't write about Life; he writes about other people who make fifty thousand dollars a year; he writes about a bunch of rich corpses and, generally speaking, he is a rich corpse himself. Not me, though. Not Saroyan. This play is lyric and simple and alive.

It says just exactly what it means. When the boy in this play dynamites his grandmother because he needs some money to get gin, that is something real. When he puts a nickel in the piano for music, that is real too. When he meets the society girl and says, "How's chances, sister?" and she answers, "OK, Mac," that is a real, lovely, and heartbreaking thing.

In the plays about the rich corpses it takes three acts and about sixty thousand dollars' worth of scenery to get around to a beautiful and natural request like that, and half the time nothing comes of it, either.

II

I am a warm, rich, passionate human being and very few things are too much for me. Not even dramatic criticism. When a man writes in a newspaper or a magazine that he doesn't understand this play or is bored by it, that is all right with me. It is hard to imagine anybody not liking something that is as eloquent and native and true as a child running after a butterfly or a coloured man scratching himself, but I do not get sore. I am just sorry for the crazy bastard.

III

The following are excerpts from some of the reviews published in the New York Press:

RICHARD WATTS, Jr., *Herald Tribune*: It is a darling play . . . but we must not ignore the Chinese.

BROOKS ATKINSON, *Times*: Lit with the same ineluctable fire that once informed the witches and the cauldron on the heath.

JOHN MASON BROWN, *Post*: Challenges the best of Aristophanes, Gogol, Pirandello, Racine, and the Song of Solomon.

SIDNEY B. WHIPPLE, *World-Telegram*: Either Saroyan is crazy . . . or I am. A child has done this horrid thing.

IV

This play was written in an hour and a half with a quill pen I generally keep in a little bowl of bird shot. For a man like me, an original, talented, profound, sensitive, and humorous Armenian, a typewriter is an artificial barrier standing between the living brain and the clean paper. It is not for me, as the airbrush was not for Michelangelo and the adding machine was not for Euclid.

At that time I was working in Hollywood, where all authors use typewriters. "The greatest play in the world is right there on those keys, if you can only figure out how to hit them in the right order," one of them said to me. He was a man who made forty, fifty, a hundred thousand dollars a year, and he went around with a falcon on his wrist. I would rather use the quill pen. Me, personally.

V

Generally speaking, the American theatre is the aspirin of the middle classes. People go to a play because they want to get in out of the rain. Or because they have a date with some rabbit in it later on. Or just because they happen to know the Press agent and don't have to pay. It is not that way with me. I go because I love life. That is an important statement and I want to repeat it: *William Saroyan loves Life.*

In the theatre today, except in this play of mine, what you see is not Life. It is a drawing-room compromise with Life arrived at by a man who has never had to sleep in a silo or eat birch bark or trap mice to make himself a hat or any of the other brave, haunting, and sometimes foolish things people do when they don't happen to have been born on Park Avenue or in Newport, Rhode Island.

The cure for the American theatre is more plays like this one. More plays by Saroyan.

THE TIME OF *WHOSE* LIFE?

(*A dormitory at Grotton, just before vespers. Three of the boys—* JONES MINOR, FERRIS MAJOR, *and* TILDEN ELLIOTT III—*are changing from their rugger togs into their vespers togs. They are breathless and wondering, enchanted with a sweet world that also holds things like ginger beer and scones and* Esquire *magazine.* FERGUSON NICHOLSON, *the housemaster, a tall, thin man, noble because of the pain in his heart, is sitting in one corner, reading* Variety *and drinking a dry Martini. In another corner an old graduate, mad and very dirty, is throwing cards into a hat. A scrubwoman comes in. A lifetime of toil, including six years with the Shuberts, has not quenched her brimming and precious spirit.*)

SCRUBWOMAN (*compassionate, supernatural; the Earth Mother*): How about sweeping up around here, gents? Get some of the fug out of the joint.

JONES MINOR: Sweep. You won't sweep the torture and despair of Life from the heart with a broom . . .

FERRIS MAJOR: Or the beauty of it either.

OLD GRADUATE (*lost in his eternal dream of the past*): Dissolute and damned. Both the student body and the faculty.

HOUSEMASTER: Elliott.

ELLIOTT: Yes, sir?

HOUSEMASTER: Go down to the Greek's and get me two ham sandwiches and a billiard ball.

ELLIOTT (*uneasily*): What for?

HOUSEMASTER (*watching the scrubwoman; fascinated by the unique, all-female, and mysterious experiences once enjoyed somewhere in the world by this scrubwoman*): Ham on white. British mustard.

ELLIOTT (*still puzzled, but going out dutifully*): A cue ball?

HOUSEMASTER: No, the red one. (*To the* SCRUBWOMAN; *waving the cocktail-shaker*): Martini?

SCRUBWOMAN: No, thanks, pal. The Head don't like us to drink on duty.

HOUSEMASTER: You're missing a lot. *I'm* always drunk. The days and nights are whittling me away, and—(*he breaks off as the* HEADMASTER, *a quiet, grave man, carrying a bridle, comes into the cubicle*). Were you looking for something, sir?

HEADMASTER (*genially*): Ah, Nicholson. Fried again, I see. (*With a change of mood, sternly*): Ferris Major!

FERRIS MAJOR (*springing up, dynamic, translated*): Sir?

HEADMASTER: Is there a polo pony in this room?

FERRIS MAJOR: A what, sir?

HEADMASTER (*going to a closet, opening it, and discovering a polo pony*): As I thought. You know the rules, I believe, Ferris. No polo ponies or young women in dorm after four o'clock.

FERRIS MAJOR (*in a low voice, accepting his doom*): Yes, sir.

HEADMASTER: This means birching, of course. (*He goes out, leading the polo pony; fatal, inexorable, the Scourge of God.*)

OLD GRADUATE (*throwing the ace of spades at the hat*): Dissolute and damned. Both the student body and the faculty.

HOUSEMASTER (*still preoccupied by the scrubwoman; the strange, illict, bygone adventures of the scrubwoman*): I drink to your unconquerable spirit, Mrs Le Bogan.

SCRUBWOMAN: My name ain't Mrs Le Bogan.

HOUSEMASTER: Then Guinevere or Heloise. In any case, I drink. To your ancient sins, Faustine.

SCRUBWOMAN: Listen, what the hell you talking about?

HOUSEMASTER (*wearily*): I don't know. What do any of us talk about? Love. Happiness. Towering injustice everywhere. The game with St Paul's. (*Furiously, draining the Martini*) How the hell do I know? What do *you* talk about?

SCRUBWOMAN (*sly, roguish, Salome, old but not regenerate*): Jeez, I dunno, mister. Harry K. Thaw. The time we burned up the city of Chicago. Shooting Garfield. All like that.

HOUSEMASTER: Life! The terror and the wonder and the beauty of it. (*Gathering momentum*) Life! *Life!* LIFE!

(*As he goes on, ELLIOTT re-enters with the sandwiches and the billiard ball; the SCRUBWOMAN wrings out her mop and starts to wipe up the floors; the old graduate opens another pack of cards and begins throwing them at the hat; JONES MINOR and FERRIS MAJOR gather up their hymnals and prayer books; the polo pony trots in through the door and back into the closet. Life has come full circle.*)

OLD GRADUATE (*sombre, triumphant; his opinion of everything borne out*): Dissolute and damned. Both the student body and the faculty.

(*From the courtyard the bell for vespers sounds, very wonderful and sad. The curtain falls.*)

S. J. Perelman

THOSE WHO recall the early Marx Brothers films, with their explosive dialogue and surrealist imagery—vintage films such as *Animal Crackers*, *Duck Soup*, and *Monkey Business*—may be excused for not noticing, in more than one of these pictures, the name of Perelman among those responsible for what was loosely called the Screenplay.

I never noticed it myself, and I have since discovered nothing relevant about Perelman except what he has written about himself in two recent and unlikely travelogues. But I have, nevertheless, a healthy respect for Perelman. He has received the usual encomiums about being 'America's Funniest Humorist', or titles to that effect. But I prefer the tribute of a critic in the *New York Times*:

> The master of every cliché in the English language, Perelman runs through them backwards, as witches do in the Lord's Prayer, producing in the reader's mind a pleasant daze similar to that experienced by users of cocaine. He is a stylist whose style is absolutely indescribable. . . .

Well, then, let us not try to describe it. (Apart from making it quite clear that the style skids off at a tangent, and that no holds are barred once the battle with the language has commenced.) To take an example—the opening salvo from Perelman's first book to appear in England, *Crazy Like a Fox*:

> Yesterday morning I awoke from a deep dream of peace compounded of equal parts of allonal and Vat 69 to find that autumn was indeed here.

Here is Perelman's cocksure, cockeyed approach to life, in all its brilliance and weakness. Brilliant, because he knows his stuff, and could probably have been an informed, sensitive writer instead of a licensed lunatic from the *New Yorker*. Weak, in my estimation, because he throws in so many trade-names and local references that not more than a quota of his material is really for export. It's no use expecting that you will understand Perelman's frequent, obscure references if Macy's is the only American store you know, and if you are not well up in New York street plans and Hollywood jargon. Taken in bulk, Perelman can be tiresome, but I know of few bedside books quite as insomniac as his (if there is such a word). Perelman called his trilogy of humour 'A Child's Garden of Curses', and for a long while I wondered why. Perhaps it is because he wants us to believe there's, if not method, at least morality in his madness, and that, as one critic wrote of him, 'The whole area of our foolishness is his target'.

But this is dangerous ground. I prefer my Perelman as it comes, in small but lethal doses. 'Strictly From Hunger' ought to spring from his experiences in Hollywood, but I doubt if it does. It is, like most of Perelman's work, rather akin to going on what the Americans call a roller-coaster. And 'Waiting for Santy' shows him as a parodist—a pleasantly dated piece, this, but one which would suit either the Marx Brothers or the Goons.

❧

WAITING FOR SANTY

(*A Christmas Playlet*)

(With a bow to Mr Clifford Odets)

The sweatshop of S. Claus, a manufacturer of children's toys on North Pole Street. Time: the night before Christmas.

At rise, seven gnomes, RANKIN, PANKEN, RIVKIN, RISKIN, RUSKIN, BRISKIN, *and* PRASKIN, *are discovered working furiously to fill orders piling up at stage right. The whir of lathes, the hum of motors, and the hiss of drying lacquer are so deafening that at times the dialogue cannot be heard, which is very vexing if you vex easily.* (*Note:* The parts of RANKIN, PANKEN, RIVKIN, RISKIN, RUSKIN, BRISKIN, *and* PRASKIN *are interchangeable, and may be secured directly from your dealer or the factory.*)

RISKIN (*filing a Meccano girder, bitterly*): A parasite, a leech, a bloodsucker—altogether a five-star nogoodnick! Starvation wages we get so he can ride around in a red team with reindeers!

RUSKIN (*jeering*): Hey, Karl Marx, whyntcha hire a hall?

RISKIN (*sneering*): Scab! Stool pigeon! Company spy!

(They tangle and rain blows on each other. While waiting for these to dry, each returns to his respective task.)

BRISKIN *(sadly to* PANKEN*)*: All day long I'm painting 'Snow Queen' on these Flexible Flyers and my little Irving lays in a cold tenement with the gout.

PANKEN: You said before it was the mumps.

BRISKIN *(with a fatalistic shrug)*: The mumps—the gout—go argue with City Hall.

PANKEN *(kindly, passing him a bowl)*: Here, take a piece fruit.

BRISKIN *(chewing)*: It ain't bad, for wax fruit.

PANKEN *(with pride)*: I painted it myself.

BRISKIN *(rejecting the fruit)*: Ptoo! Slave psychology!

RIVKIN *(suddenly, half to himself, half to the Party)*: I got a belly full of stars, baby. You make me feel like I swallowed a Roman candle.

PRASKIN *(curiously)*: What's wrong with the kid?

RISKIN: What's wrong with all of us? The system! Two years he and Claus's daughter's been making googoo eyes behind the old man's back.

PRASKIN: So what!

RISKIN *(scornfully)*: So what? Economic determinism! What do you think the kid's name is—J. Pierpoint Rivkin? He ain't even got enough for a bottle of Dr Brown's Celery Tonic. I tell you, it's like gall in my mouth two young people shouldn't have a room where they could make great music.

RANKIN *(warningly)*: Shhh! Here she comes now! (STELLA CLAUS *enters, carrying a portable phonograph. She and* RIVKIN *embrace, place a record on the turntable, and begin a very slow waltz, unmindful that the phonograph is playing* 'Cohen on the Telephone'.)

STELLA *(dreamily)*: Love me, sugar?

RIVKIN: I can't sleep, I can't eat, that's how I love you. You're a double malted with two scoops of whipped cream; you're the moon rising over Mosholu Parkway; you're a two weeks' vacation at Camp Nitgedaiget! I'd pull down the Chrysler Building to make a bobbie pin for your hair.

STELLA: I've got a stomach full of anguish. Oh, Rivvy, what'll we do?

PANKEN *(sympathetically)*: Here, try a piece fruit.

RIVKIN *(fiercely)*: Wax fruit—that's been my whole life! Imitations! Substitutes! Well, I'm through! Stella, tonight I'm

160

telling your old man. He can't play mumblety-peg with two human beings! (*The tinkle of sleigh bells is heard offstage, followed by a voice shouting,* "Whoa, Dasher! Whoa, Dancer!" *A moment later* S. CLAUS *enters in a gust of mock snow. He is a pompous bourgeois of sixty-five who affects a white beard and a false air of benevolence. But tonight the ruddy colour is missing from his cheeks, his step falters, and he moves heavily. The gnomes hastily replace the marzipan they have been filching.*)

STELLA (*anxiously*): Papa! What did the specialist say to you?

CLAUS (*brokenly*): The biggest professor in the country . . . the best cardiac man that money could buy . . . I tell you I was like a wild man.

STELLA: Pull yourself together, Sam!

CLAUS: It's no good. Adhesions, diabetes, sleeping sickness, decalcomania—oh, my God! I got to cut out climbing in chimneys, he says—me, Sanford Claus, the biggest toy concern in the world!

STELLA (*soothingly*): After all, it's only one man's opinion.

CLAUS: No, no, he cooked my goose. I'm like a broken uke after a Yosian picnic. Rivkin!

RIVKIN: Yes, Sam.

CLAUS: My boy, I had my eye on you for a long time. You and Stella thought you were too foxy for an old man, didn't you? Well, let bygones be bygones. Stella, do you love this gnome?

STELLA (*simply*): He's the whole stage show at the Music Hall, Papa; he's Toscanini conducting Beethoven's Fifth; he's——

CLAUS (*curtly*): Enough already. Take him. From now on he's a partner in the firm. (*As all exclaim,* CLAUS *holds up his hand for silence.*) And tonight he can take my route and make the deliveries. It's the least I could do for my own flesh and blood. (*As the happy couple kiss,* CLAUS *wipes away a suspicious moisture and turns to the other gnomes.*) Boys, do you know what day tomorrow is?

GNOMES (*crowding around expectantly*): Christmas!

CLAUS: Correct. When you look in your envelopes tonight you'll find a little present from me—forty per cent pay cut. And the first one who opens his trap—gets this.

(*As he holds up a tear-gas bomb and beams at them the gnomes utter cries of joy, join hands, and dance around him shouting exultantly.*

All except RIVKIN *and* BRISKIN, *that is, who exchange a quick glance and go underground.*)

STRICTLY FROM HUNGER

Yes, I was excited, and small wonder. What boy wouldn't be, boarding a huge, mysterious, puffing steam train for golden California? As Mamma adjusted my reefer and strapped on my leggings, I almost burst with impatience. Grinning red-caps lifted my luggage into the compartment and spat on it. Mamma began to weep into the small pillowcase she had brought along for the purpose.

"Oh, son, I wish you hadn't become a scenario writer!" she sniffled.

"Aw, now, Mom," I comforted her, "it's no worse than playing the piano on a call-house." She essayed a brave little smile, and, reaching into her reticule, produced a flat package which she pressed into my hands. For a moment I was puzzled, then I cried out with glee.

"Jelly sandwiches! Oh, Moms!"

"Eat them all, boy o'mine," she told me; "they're good for boys with hollow little legs." Tenderly she pinned to my lapel the green tag reading 'To Plushnick Productions, Hollywood, California'. The whistle shrilled, and in a moment I was chugging out of Grand Central's dreaming spires followed only by the anguished cries of relatives who would now have to go to work. I had chugged only a few feet when I realized that I had left without the train, so I had to run back and wait for it to start.

As we sped along the glorious fever spots of the Hudson I decided to make a tour of inspection. To my surprise I found that I was in the only passenger car of the train; the other cars were simply dummies snipped out of cardboard and painted to simulate coaches. Even 'passengers' had been cunningly drawn in coloured crayons in the 'window', as well as ragged tramps clinging to the blinds below and drinking Jamaica ginger. With a rueful smile I returned to my seat and gorged myself on Jelly sandwiches.

At Buffalo the two other passengers and I discovered to our horror that the conductor had been left behind. We finally decided to divide up his duties; I punched the tickets, the old lady opposite me wore a conductor's hat and locked the washroom as we came into stations, and the young man who looked as if his feet were not mates consulted a Hamilton watch frequently. But we missed the conductor's earthy conversation and it was not until we had exchanged several questionable stories that we began to forget our loss.

A flicker of interest served to shorten the trip. At Fort Snodgrass, Ohio, two young and extremely polite road-agents boarded the train and rifled us of our belongings. They explained that they were modern Robin Hoods and were stealing from the poor to give to the rich. They had intended to rape all the women and depart for Sherwood Forest, but when I told them that Sherwood Forest as well as the women were in England, their chagrin was comical in the extreme. They declined my invitation to stay and take a chance on the train's pool, declaring that the engineer had fixed the run and would fleece us, and got off at South Bend with every good wish.

The weather is always capricious in the Middle West, and although it was midsummer, the worst blizzard in Chicago's history greeted us on our arrival. The streets were crowded with thousands of newsreel cameramen trying to photograph one another bucking the storm on the Lake Front. It was a novel idea for the newsreels and I wished them well. With only two hours in Chicago I would be unable to see the city, and the thought drew me into a state of composure. I noted with pleasure that a fresh coat of grime had been given to the Dearborn Street station, though I was hardly vain enough to believe that it had anything to do with my visit. There was the usual ten-minute wait while the porters withdrew with my portable typewriter to a side room and flailed it with hammers, and at last I was aboard the 'Sachem', crack train of the B.B.D. & O. lines.

It was as if I had suddenly been transported into another world. 'General Crook', in whom I was to make my home for the next three days, and his two neighbours, 'Lake Tahoe' and 'Chief Malomai', were everything that the word 'Pullman' implies; they were Pullmans. Uncle Eben, in charge of 'General Crook', informed me that the experiment of air-cooling cars had been so successful that the road intended trying to heat them next winter.

"Ah suttinly looks fo'd to dem roastin' cars Ah's gwine

have next winter, he, he, he!" he chuckled, rubbing soot into my hat.

The conductor told me he had been riding on trains for so long that he had begun to smell like one, and sure enough, two brakemen waved their lanterns at him that night and tried to tempt him down a siding in Kansas City. We became good friends and it came as something of a blow when I heard next morning that he had fallen off the train during the night. The fireman said that we had circled about for an hour trying to find him but that it had been impossible to lower a boat because we did not carry a boat.

The run was marked by only one incident out of the ordinary. I had ordered breaded veal cutlet the first evening, and my waiter, poking his head into the kitchen, had repeated the order. The cook, unfortunately, understood him to say 'dreaded veal cutlet', and resenting the slur, sprang at the waiter with drawn razor. In a few seconds I was the only living remnant of the shambles, and at Topeka I was compelled to wait until a new shambles was hooked on and I proceeded with dinner.

It seemed only a scant week or ten days before we were pulling into Los Angeles. I had grown so attached to my porter that I made him give me a lock of his hair. I wonder if he still has the ten-cent piece I gave him? There was a gleam in his eye which could only have been insanity as he leaned over me. Ah, Uncle Eben, faithful old retainer, where are you now? Gone to what obscure ossuary? If this should chance to meet your kindly gaze, drop me a line care of *Variety*, won't you? They know what to do with it.

II

The violet hush of twilight was descending over Los Angeles as my hostess, Violet Hush, and I left the suburbs headed toward Hollywood. In the distance a glow of huge piles of burning motion-picture scripts lit up the sky. The crisp tang of frying writers and directors whetted my appetite. How good it was to be alive, I thought, inhaling deep lungfuls of carbon monoxide. Suddenly our powerful Gatti-Cazazza slid to a stop in the traffic.

"What is it, Jenkin?" Violet called anxiously through the speaking-tube to the chauffeur (played by Lyle Talbot).

A suttee was in progress by the roadside, he said—did we wish to see it? Quickly Violet and I elbowed our way through the crowd. An enormous funeral pyre composed of thousands of feet of film and scripts, drenched with Chanel Number Five, awaited the torch of Jack Holt, who was to act as master of ceremonies. In a few terse words Violet explained this unusual custom borrowed from the Hindus and never paid for. The worst disgrace that can befall a producer is an unkind notice from a New York reviewer. When this happens, the producer becomes a pariah in Hollywood. He is shunned by his friends, thrown into bankruptcy, and like a Japanese electing hara-kiri, he commits suttee. A great bonfire is made of the film, and the luckless producer, followed by directors, actors, technicians, and the producer's wives, immolate themselves. Only the scenario writers are exempt. These are tied between the tails of two spirited Caucasian ponies, which are then driven off in opposite directions. This custom is called 'a conference'.

Violet and I watched the scene breathlessly. Near us Harry Cohn, head of Columbia Studios, was being rubbed with huck towels preparatory to throwing himself into the flames. He was nonchalantly smoking a Rocky Ford five-centre, and the man's courage drew a tear to the eye of even the most callous. Weeping relatives besought him to eschew his design, but he stood adamant. Adamant Eve, his plucky secretary, was being rubbed with crash towels preparatory to flinging herself into Cohn's embers. Assistant directors busily prepared spears, war-bonnets, and bags of pemmican which the Great Chief would need on his trip to the 'Happy Hunting Grounds'. Wampas and beads to placate the Great Spirit (played by Will Hays) were piled high about the stoical tribesman.

Suddenly Jack Holt (played by Edmund Lowe) raised his hand for silence. The moment had come. With bowed head Holt made a simple invocation couched in one-syllable words so that even the executives might understand. Throwing his five-centre to a group of autograph-hunters, the great man poised himself for the fatal leap. But from off-scene came the strident clatter of coconut shells, and James Agee, Filmdom's fearless critic, wearing the uniform of a Confederate guerrilla and the whiskers of General Beauregard, galloped in on a foam-flecked pinto. It was he whose mocking review had sent

Cohn into Coventry. It was a dramatic moment as the two stood pitted against each other—Cohn against Agee, the Blue against the Grey. But with true Southern gallantry Agee was the first to extend the hand of friendship.

"Ah reckon it was an unworthy slur, suh," he said in manly tones. "Ah-all thought you-all's pictuah was lousy but it opened at the Rialto to sensational grosses, and Ah-all 'pologizes. Heah, have a yam." And he drew a yam from his tunic. Not to be outdone in hospitality, Cohn drew a yam from his tunic, and soon they were exchanging yams and laughing over the old days.

When Violet and I stole away to our waiting motor, we felt that we were somehow nearer to each other. I snuggled luxuriously into the buffalo lap-robe Violet had provided against the treacherous night air and gazed out at the gleaming neon lights. Soon we would be in Beverly Hills, and already the quaint native women were swarming alongside in their punts urging us to buy their cunning beadwork and mangoes. Occasionally I threw a handful of coppers to the Negro boys, who dived for them joyfully. The innocent squalls of the policemen as the small blackamoors pinched them were irresistible. Unable to resist them, Violet and I were soon pinching each other till our skins glowed. Violet was good to the touch, with a firm, fleshy texture like a winesap or pippin. It seemed but a moment before we were sliding under the *porte-cochère* of her home, a magnificent rambling structure of beaver-board patterned after an Italian ropewalk of the sixteenth century. It had recently been remodelled by a family of wrens who had introduced chewing-gum into the left wing, and only three or four obscure Saxon words could do it justice.

I was barely warming my hands in front of the fire and watching Jimmy Fidler turn on a spit when my presence on the Pacific Slope made itself felt. The news of my arrival had thrown international financial centres into an uproar, and sheaves of wires, cables, phone messages, and even corn began piling up. An ugly rumour that I might reorganize the motion-picture industry was being bruited about in the world's commodity markets. My brokers, Whitelipped & Trembling, were beside themselves. The New York Stock Exchange was begging them for assurances of stability and

Threadneedle Street awaited my next move with drumming pulses. Film shares ricocheted sharply, although wools and meats were sluggish, if not downright sullen. To the reporters who flocked around me I laughingly disclaimed that this was a business trip. I was simply a scenario writer to whom the idea of work was abhorrent. A few words murmured into the transatlantic telephone, the lift of an eyebrow here, the shrug of a shoulder there, and equilibrium was soon restored. I washed sparsely, curled my moustache with a heated hairpin, flicked a drop of Sheik Lure on my lapel, and rejoined my hostess.

After a copious dinner, melting-eyed beauties in lacy black underthings fought with each other to serve me kummel. A hurried apology, and I was curled up in bed with the autumn 1927 issue of *The Yale Review*. Half way through an exciting symposium of Sir Thomas Aquinas' indebtedness to Professors Whitehead and Spengler, I suddenly detected a stowaway blonde under the bed. Turning a deaf ear to her heartrending entreaties and burning glances, I sent her packing. Then I treated my face to a feast of skin food, buried my head in the pillow and went bye-bye.

III

Hollywood Boulevard! I rolled the rich syllables over on my tongue and thirstily drank in the beauty of the scene before me. On all sides nattily attired boulevarders clad in rich stuffs strolled nonchalantly, inhaling cubebs and exchanging epigrams stolen from Martial and Wilde. Thousands of scantily draped but none the less appetizing girls milled past me, their mouths a scarlet wound and their eyes clearly defined in their faces. Their voluptuous curves set my blood on fire, and as I made my way down Mammary Lane, a strange thought began to invade my brain: I realized that I had not eaten breakfast yet. In a Chinese eatery cunningly built in the shape of an old shoe, I managed to assuage the inner man with a chopped glove salad topped off with frosted cocoa. Charming platinum-haired hostesses in red pyjamas and peaked caps added a note of colour to the surroundings, whilst a gypsy orchestra played selections from Victor Herbert's operettas on musical saws. It was a bit of old Vienna come to life, and the sun was a red ball in the heavens before I realized with a start that I had promised to report at the Plushnick Studios.

Commandeering a taxicab, I arrived at the studio just in time to witness the impressive ceremony of changing the guard. In the central parade ground, on a snowy white charger, sat Max Plushnick, resplendent in a producer's uniform, his chest glittering with first mortgage liens, amortizations, and estoppels. His personal guard, composed of picked vice-presidents of the Chase National Bank, was drawn up stiffly about him in a hollow square.

But the occasion was not a happy one. A writer had been caught trying to create an adult picture. The drums rolled dismally and the writer, his head sunk on his chest, was led out amid a ghastly silence. With the aid of a small step-ladder Plushnick slid lightly from his steed. Sternly he ripped the epaulettes and buttons from the traitor's tunic, broke his sword across his knee, and in a few harsh words demoted him to the mail department.

"And now," began Plushnick, "I further condemn you to eat . . ."

"No, no!" screamed the poor wretch, falling to his knees and embracing Plushnick's jack boots, "not that, not that!"

"Stand up, man," ordered Plushnick, his lip curling. "I condemn you to eat in the studio restaurant for ten days, and may God have mercy on your soul." The awful words rang out on the evening air and even Plushnick's hardened old mercenaries shuddered. The heartrending cries of the unfortunate were drowned in the boom of the sunset gun.

In the wardrobe department I was photographed, fingerprinted, and measured for the smock and Windsor tie which was to be my uniform. A nameless fear clutched at my heart as two impassive turnkeys herded me down a corridor to my supervisor's office. For what seemed hours we waited in an ante-room. Then my serial number was called, the leg-irons were struck off, and I was shoved through a door into the presence of Diana ffrench-Mamoulian.

How to describe what followed? Diana ffrench-Mamoulian was accustomed to having her way with writers, and my long lashes and peachbloom mouth seemed to whip her to insensate desire. In vain, time and again, I tried to bring her attention back to the story we were discussing, only to find her gem-encrusted fingers straying through my hair. When our inter-view was over, her cynical attempt to 'date me up' made every fibre in my being cry out in revolt.

"P-please," I stammered, my face burning. "I-I wish you wouldn't . . . I'm engaged to a Tri Kappa at Goucher——"

"Just one kiss," she pleaded, her breath hot against my neck. In desperation I granted her boon, knowing full well that my weak defences were crumbling before the onslaught of this love tigress. Finally she allowed me to leave, but only after I had promised to dine at her pent-house apartment and have an intimate chat about the script. The basket of slave bracelets and marzipan I found awaiting me on my return home made me realize to what lengths Diana would go.

I was radiant that night in blue velvet tails and a bouton-niere of diamonds from Cartier's, my eyes starry and the merest hint of cologne at my ear-lobes. An inscrutable Oriental served the Lucullan repast and my vis-à-vis was as effervescent as the wine.

"Have a bit of the wine, darling?" queried Diana solici-tously, indicating the roast Long Island aeroplane with apple-sauce. I tried to turn our conversation from the personal note, but Diana would have none of it. Soon we were exchanging gay banter over the mellow Vouvray, laughing as we dipped fastidious fingers into the Crisco parfait for which Diana was famous. Our meal finished we sauntered into the rumpus room and Diana turned on the radio. With a savage snarl the radio turned on her and we slid over the waxed floor in the intricate maze of the jackdaw strut. Without quite knowing why, I found myself hesitating before the plate of liqueur candies Diana was pressing on me.

"I don't think I should—really, I'm a trifle faint——"

"Oh, come on," she urged masterfully. "After all, you're old enough to be your father—I mean, I'm old enough to be my mother . . ." She stuffed a brandy bonbon between my clenched teeth. Before long I was eating them thirstily, reeling about the room and shouting snatches of coarse, drunken dog-gerel. My brain was on fire, I tell you. Through the haze I saw Diana ffrench-Mamoulian, her nostrils dilated, groping for me. My scream of terror only egged her on, overturning chairs and tables in her bestial pursuit. With superhuman talons she tore off my collar and suspenders. I sank to my knees, choked with sobs, hanging on to my last shirt-stud like a drowning man. Her Svengali eyes were slowly hypnotizing me; I fought like a wounded bird—and then blissful unconsciousness.

When I came to, the Oriental servant and Diana were battling in the centre of the floor. As I watched, Yen Shee Gow drove a well-aimed blow to her mid-section, following it with a right cross to the jaw. Diana staggered and rolled under the table. Before my astonished eyes John Chinaman stripped the mask from his face and revealed the features of Blanche Almonds, a little seamstress I had long wooed unsuccessfully in New York. Gently she bathed my temples with Florida water and explained how she had followed me, suspecting Diana ffrench-Mamoulian's intentions. I let her rain kisses over my face and lay back in her arms as beaming Ivan tucked us in and cracked his whip over the prancing bays. In a few seconds our sleigh was skimming over the hard crust towards Port Arthur and freedom, leaving Plushnick's discomfited officers gnashing one another's teeth. The wintry Siberian moon glowed over the tundras, drenching my hair with moonbeams for Blanche to kiss away. And so, across the silvery steppes amid the howling of wolves, we rode into a new destiny, purified in the crucible that men call Hollywood.

Jane Allen

HOLLYWOOD HAS always been a sitting target for most American satirists. Apart from S. J. Perelman, and the licensed jesters of the film world itself, permitted to foul their own luxurious nest, I can recall the early delights of a book by Elmer Rice, *A Voyage to Purilia*, in which an innocent beheld life according to the ethics of the cinema; a third-degree examination by one Budd Schulberg, *What Makes Sammy Run*; and a novel called *I Lost My Girlish Laughter* by Jane Allen.

Miss Allen may, indeed, have sustained this loss in her engaging account, but we, meanwhile, have lost Miss Allen. She has not, to my knowledge, come up again for air (perhaps, like Anita Loos and Dorothy Parker, she married into films), but this description of a Hollywood cinema magnate having his wife's baby is too good to miss.

⊰⊱

IT'S WONDERFUL TO BE A MOTHER

December 3rd

DEAR LIZ,

I have just become a mother so if you ever have a relapse and decide you are fed up on being an independent woman of the world and think that you need the little patter of feet to make you complete, harken to me.

It is a great joy but it is all very expensive. You begin payment from the moment you start losing your figure. Once however you have passed through this trying ordeal, the real pay-off commences. The attending physician will guarantee to bring little Oscar into the world for not a cent under $2,000. But there are consultants. These are very superior gentlemen who go into conference with your own physician and corroborate his testimony that you are really going to have a baby. That costs $50 a visit. The suite at the hospital is a mere $35 a day. There are also nurses, day and night ones, and a little

171

thing called extras which usually becomes the main item on your bill.

Now we come to the layette. If you have a lot of relatives, it is fairly simple, but since you are supporting most of them you buy all your own layette. This layette consists of all sorts of dresses and didies (monogrammed) and cummerbunds and whatnots, to say nothing of a beautiful English bassinet all upholstered in satin with fleecy titbits to cover. All in all you can't get out under a round thousand even though your baby will grow out of these in a few months.

Then there is a nursery. Oh, I know you and I didn't have one when we were toddlers, but have you ever fully considered the importance of sunshine to a growing child? Just tossing it out into the backyard isn't going to help because it might get sunstroke or a variety of germs. So you summon a flock of architects to draw you some designs for a nursery all encased in a special infra-ray glass that will let in the good rays and keep out the evil ones. If you are lucky, you will pick the architect who has a sister-in-law who knows she would be a wow in pictures, so instead of charging you the usual cost plus ten per cent plus anything else he can collect, he will just charge you a paltry five grand and guarantee that your child will have the most modern, up-to-date, germ-proof, fun-proof, and burglar-proof mausoleum. Of course, there is a starched *femme* who must come home with little Oscar and is very costly and haughty and won't let you near him for fear of contamination. Sometimes the awful thought strikes me that it is pure dumb luck that you and I are still alive and apparently in possession of most of our faculties.

Six am this morning I am routed out of my bed and rushed to the hospital in order to hold Mr Brand's hand. It seems he is disconsolate what with the hospital staff in Mrs Brand's room and nobody around to cheer him.

For a quiet half hour I sit beside Mr Brand and permit him to clutch my arm, while doctors and nurses flit past us with very grave faces relaxing only occasionally to give the anxious father an indulgent smile or two. But little Oscar after the first fright relaxes, probably chuckling to himself that already he has put one over on the old man.

Everyone relaxes in general with the exception of Mr Brand, who proceeds to have a nervous collapse and yells hoarsely for an MD. A sedative is administered to him by the chief of staff himself and after a gurgle or two and a flutter of his eyelids, he decides to live. This makes for a nice pause so that Dr X can engage Mr Brand in conversation and ask him why it is that producers are all the time making medical pictures that are not authentic? Now he can tell Mr Brand some stories about experiences he has had that would make the most marvellous pictures. Some day he says he will maybe take time off to do just that little thing, dash off a story or two just to show the industry. He knows he can write for he has published quite a lot of stuff already in the medical journals.

Mr Brand wears a strained expression something like a man who has just come out from under fire and is trying to readjust himself to normal life once more but doesn't quite contact. He doesn't appear to hear what the doctor is saying, which perhaps is just as well because he might become violent. I stare at my somnambulent boss and become perturbed. Maybe he will not come out of this coma. I recall cases of shell shock and remember that cures have been effected by rousing the patient through further shock. I toy with the idea of taking desperate measures and ponder on going into a cataleptic fit myself.

Then, like a sleepwalker awakening, Mr Brand shudders. He makes a few pathetic passes with a limp hand over his face. Is it possible, I think, that this man can really be deeply affected like other normal human beings by the primitive forces of life?

Then bingo! The Brand body shakes itself into reality and we are off! "Get me Wardrobe! Call off my luncheon appointment with Tarn; get me Cahan on long distance; find a room here where I can work; find a room where you can work (meaning me); get a room where Tussler and Skinner can work. I want them here!" I do not stop to question him. I do not say, "Mr Brand, this is a hospital and not a hotel." I fly. For it seems that not only am I to co-operate in having Mr Brand's baby, but I also must assist in keeping the wheels of production humming so that Sarya Tarn, like Oscar, can be launched. I am at the door when he yells ". . . and have Palmer here ready to send out announcements to the papers about the baby!" So you can see he still remembers that he is going to become a father.

I hie me to the business office. I want some rooms, I say,

nice quiet rooms where our production staff can operate. The business office looks at me peculiarly. Now, now, they calm me. You don't need a lot of rooms. All you need is a nice quiet bed, and we can fix you up very comfortably in the ward. I see they think I am a mental case. I explain who I am and why we have to have some rooms. The words 'Brand' and 'pictures' are magic. Unfortunately, however, it seems the hospital is full of a lot of patients. There is a lady in maternity, though, who will be leaving shortly and Mr Brand can have her room. In the meantime we will have to use the solarium. It is pleasant and sunny up there. I put in some calls for the studio and report back to S. B.

He is in a complaining mood. He doesn't like the way the hospital is run. The floors are slippery. Why don't they have carpets? What if a nurse fell while carrying an infant?

I quietly point out to him that hospitals must be antiseptic and that rugs are nice warm breeding-places for germs.

I think it is a good point. He thinks they could do something about it.

I search for an antidote and hit upon the brilliant idea that he may be hungry. How about some breakfast? He brightens. So I telephone the kitchen and they are very cordial and say they will send up a tray immediately.

While we wait I take down a few letters and complaints. When an orderly comes in with a tray, I give one sniff and feel faint myself, for it is full of appetizing ham and eggs. But Mr Brand doesn't react favourably. He sneers. He can't eat that stuff. "Call the Brown Derby," he yells at me, "and have them send up a mushroom omelette. Remember to tell them it's for Brand." "What about this tray?" I ask. "Oh, you can have it," says Mr Brand. So I do.

I have barely finished my repast when a wild-eyed orderly bursts in. The telephone girl, he says, is going berserk. It seems that everyone at Super Films is on the 'phone all at once trying to get hold of Mr Brand and they all say it is a matter of life and death.

"Can't a man have a baby in peace?" howls Mr Brand.

But it seems he can't, for there are a lot of other people who have babies and people who are ill and their friends have 'phones and would like to know how they are, so the switchboard can't all the time be answering calls for Mr Brand. The orderly explains this just as politely as he can. "My God," groans Mr Brand. "Do I have to worry about that too? Get another switchboard," he roars. "Get another telephone girl."

So it is up to me to take the orderly by the hand and lead him to the switchboard, where we all go into a huddle. We have about completed negotiations when I sense an alien atmosphere in the room and look up to find Jim Palmer.

"Hello, toots," he says vulgarly.

I am very pleased to see him, for somehow even if Jim Palmer is a screwball he has a soothing effect on me.

No, my dove, it is not an amorous feeling he evokes. On the contrary. He is to me what a prairie oyster is to you after a big night—exotic to the taste, but very clarifying to the mind.

"I am certainly glad to see you," I say with utmost cordiality.

"This is a break," he says. "It must be that hospitals have a sentimental effect on you. How about dinner with me tonight in the emergency ward?"

"That will be very cosy," I say, "for doubtless unless little Oscar chooses to make his debut shortly, we are going to take a long-term option on this hospital."

"So," he snorts, "little Oscar is holding up production, is he? That must be a blow to Brand. Hasn't he asked you to do something about it, Maggie?"

"Darling," I say sweetly, "I'd have the baby myself if I could end this suspense, but in the meantime we had better present ourselves to the great man. . . ."

"Yeah, before he signs up all the nurses on the maternity floor."

In the solarium an old man in a wheel-chair is fretting to his nurse, but otherwise the place is deserted. We make inquiries of the nurse, but she says she hasn't seen Mr Brand at all.

It occurs to me that perhaps he has been summoned to his wife's room for the announcement of the main event, but all is quiet and serene there and inquiries to the floor nurse elicit no information.

We make a grand tour of the hospital. We duck in and out of rooms; we dodge stretcher beds; wheel chairs; ether machines. All we gather in our wake are muttered imprecations and a load of anaesthetics which are suffocating. There is nothing for it but to make our way back to the solarium.

There we find Messrs Tussler and Skinner. The former is looking more dazed than ever. Why, he queries, is his presence necessary because Mr Brand is going to have a baby?

"Relax, relax," Skinner jeers at him, "and give yourself an eyeful of the girls in white. There was a honey that just came by with red hair. I'll bet she knows why she was created and for what."

"You must be patient, Skinner," Jim withers him. "Tussler has hardly been with us long enough to discover that we not only preoccupy ourselves with sex at the box-office but feel we must live life as we see it on the screen for twenty-four hours a day."

"Aw hell," says Skinner. "Even a comrade takes time out for sex."

"For the last time," cries Tussler. "I'm not . . ."

"Hi-yah, folks!"

It is Rawley of the Art Department carrying a big folder of sketches. "Where's the boss? Has the infant arrived? What goes on?"

"Make yourself at home," Jim invites. "This is a nice place to get the sun. Order up a chair and a drink and, Skinner permitting, you might get a pretty little nurse to hold your hand."

"Swell! Bring on the nurses."

The 'phone rings. I answer it. It is switchboard and she wants to know where S. B. is. Long distance is ready from New York, besides a flock of other calls from the studio and, switchboard coos at me, "Do you know that Miss Tarn just called to ask about Mrs Brand and she was the sweetest thing!"

I muffle switchboard with a few curt orders to trace Mr Brand in the hospital.

Switchboard is more than willing. She can already envisage herself ravishing an army of cameras with her profile.

"The only thing that's got her down," I tell Jim, "is that she wishes she had worn her best blue instead of that old brown thing."

"Hollywood is a wonderful place," he says dourly.

And now Eric of Wardrobe is upon us, waving a group of sketches.

"Don't you think, Mr Tussler, this would be divine for Miss

Tarn in that first sequence? It covers just enough of her to leave everything to the imagination."

"Hello, Madge," he yoo-hoos at me. "Has the little chap arrived yet?"

"No! And the big chap has disappeared," I say snappishly.

"Yo-ho! Here we come!" Props . . . and three of them are crowding into the solarium carrying wigs, weapons, and some jungle decorations.

"This is just dandy," cracks Jim. "Now we can settle ourselves to shooting the picture."

"Yeah, and where's the script?"

Roy Tyson is upon us. All we need now is Sarya and a few cameras and everything would be perfect.

"Whatdoyoumean the script?" Skinner squares off—and the battle is on—yam-yamming about what the hell does Brand expect and they are already on the fourth sequence and who in hell can turn out an Academy winner in a week.

Switchboard rings back to say she cannot locate Mr Brand but is doing everything she can and in the meantime, will I take a few calls? I hang on to the 'phone for twenty minutes and finally get hold of Bud and implore him to see that no more studio calls come through to us at the hospital unless it is *really important*!

"Okay," says Bud. "I've got everything under control."

I can tell by the tone of his voice that he is in Mr Brand's office, his legs on the desk, playing his favourite game of movie executive.

It is way past lunchtime when I get away from the 'phone and everyone is howling for food. I telephone for a flock of sandwiches and coffee and by now am in my usual limp condition.

Jim is sympathetic. "Let's duck out of this racket," he says, "and find a quiet place at the drugstore where we can have our lunch in peace."

I am very grateful to him and about to leave when switchboard rings. Mr Brand is in Room 3B on the Maternity floor and we are all to report there immediately.

There is a concerted rush to the door. We all push out into the corridor. Props drops a few spears; Tyson lets fly a manuscript; and when we make the elevator, crash goes Skinner's typewriter. He stops to pick it up while we pile into the elevator. "Hey," yells Skinner. "Wait for Baby!"

A nurse comes storming out.

"What is going on around here?" she asks grimly. "Who are you people and what are you doing here?"

Unfortunately she is neither young nor pretty, so Skinner does a casual, insolent take and shakes his head.

"Sorry, Sister, but I'm busy every night."

She does a slow burn but before she can answer there is an insistent buzz of the elevator bell and we shoot downward.

We emerge on the third floor to face an elderly and very irate nurse.

"I'm the superintendent," she advises us crisply, "and I must ask you people to remember that this is a hospital and not a motion-picture studio. You've managed to disregard that fact so far, to say nothing of insulting the nurse on the solarium floor and turning the place into a bedlam. Mr Brand is in the second room on the first left-hand turning. Now let's see how quiet you can be in getting there. There are babies on this floor and very sick women."

Even Skinner manages to subside at this, though when we turn in on the left he makes a very rude noise.

The door of Mr Brand's room is open and we all crowd in to gape at a singular spectacle.

Mr Brand, looking very droll, is in bed with a clothes-pin on his nose. In his mouth is a sort of a funnel, and a nurse stands by smiling encouragingly at him.

"Gee, are you sick, Chief?" asks Tyson feelingly.

S. B. makes vague gestures towards the clothes-pin and the funnel, indicating he cannot speak.

"Who's having this baby, anyway?" asks Skinner.

"Mr Brand is having a basal metabolism taken," explains the nurse.

S. B. nods vigorously.

"I always say," says Skinner, "that there's nothing like a little basal metabolism taken twice a day."

Mr Brand shakes his head violently.

"Hello, everybody!" Monk Faye pushes his way through to the bed and takes in the quaint tableau, especially the nurse.

"When do we test her, Brand?" he grins.

178

S. B. starts to shake his head again. The nurse removes the pin and the funnel.

"Whatthehell . . ." blusters Mr Brand. "Can't a guy be sick without a lot of cheap wisecracks? My doctor has been advising me for months to have my basal metabolism taken, and as long as I had to stay here anyway I thought it was a good time to do it. But would I get any sympathy? No! When do I have time to get away from the studio and take care of myself? What would happen if I did? I suppose if I dropped dead all you'd say is 'Poor Brand. It's too bad he had to work so hard.' "

"Gee, boss . . . the studio would go pfff . . . without you," soothes Roy.

"Thanks, Roy."

I notice the tray from the Brown Derby is by his bed untouched. I comment on this and Mr Brand says they wouldn't let him eat before he made the test. However, that reminds him he is hungry as a bear, so would I please telephone the Brown Derby and have a filet mignon sent up and some apple strudel? I do.

The nurse procures some chairs, props Mr Brand up with extra pillows, and lopes out of the room with a studied, angular stride. I have seen that lope somewhere before and suddenly remember it is peculiar to Katharine Hepburn.

"Mr Brand . . . Mr Brand." It is Eric waving frantically. "I've got to get an okay on these sketches and get back to the studio."

"All right, Eric. Let's see them."

Eric flits over to the bed and spreads out his portfolio.

S. B. turns over the pages carelessly, but his eyes are wandering doorwards. For some curious reason there are a prodigious number of nurses strutting by in eccentric attitudes. Some of them remind you of Garbo or maybe it's Crawford. However, it must be legitimate because most of them are carrying babies, hypos, or bedpans. It is all a little distracting, particularly to Mr Brand.

"No . . . I don't like 'em," says Mr Brand.

"I think they're honey," enthuses Skinner.

"Keep it clean," says Mr Brand. "I'm talking about the sketches. . . . Look, Eric, she's too dressed up for this sequence. I can't draw a line. I admit it. But I've seen pictures before, and you can't tell me that a dame in the jungle is going to wear a Chanel creation . . ."

"But, Mr Brand, this is exotic . . . this is exciting. You know perfectly well that illusion can be preserved only by covering the form." Here Eric made a few passes down his own divine form.

"It all comes down to this, Eric. I want every woman in the audience to itch to be in the jungle with nothing on, like Tarn, and I want every man to get hot."

"In other words, Eric," breaks in Jim, "Mr Brand wants you to raise a wholesale libido!"

"That's a swell word, Jim, libido. That's just what I mean. That's just what I want. It's up to you to give it to me. You'll have plenty of time in the American sequence to do a Schiaparelli."

"But there are fashions even in the jungle, Mr Brand. A woman is a woman no matter what or where . . ."

"Okay, Eric, just so long as you keep everyone conscious of the fact that she is a woman I'll be satisfied. But to hell with illusions."

Eric appeared injured.

"But, Mr Brand . . ." he starts.

"Goodbye, Eric," says the boss. "Madge, telephone the doctor and see how Mrs Brand is."

Eric shrugs his shoulders eloquently, but he gathers up his sketches and departs. I am at the 'phone learning that all is quiet on the maternal front.

"All right, Rawley; what have you got?"

Rawley spreads his layouts over the bed.

"Here's the jungle set. It's going to run a little over the budget, but you told me to go to town . . ."

"What do you mean by a little bit, Rawley?"

"Well, you see, boss, a good deal depends on where we go for location."

"Say, Monk, haven't you picked out a location yet?"

"I was in the projection room all day yesterday looking over some film the boys brought back and I would say that Ensenada's the best bet."

"But, Monk, it'll cost a fortune down there."

"Yeah, but it'll be worth it. It's just what we want."

"But, Mr Faye," says Roy, "you remember you said last

night that Catalina would be fine. You know, over by the Isthmus."

"Well, why not, Monk? Certainly it would be cheaper."

"It's all the same to me, but I like the fishing better at Ensenada," says Faye.

"That's just dandy, but we're not selling fish. We're selling motion-pictures. Roy, you see the production office and make arrangements. In the meantime when I get back to the studio I'll look at the film and let you know whether to go ahead on the Catalina location. Rawley, I'll okay these sketches if we go to Catalina, but you had better make some additional layouts and cut costs in case we have to go to Ensenada—for Monk's fishing."

Props have pushed forward now, all decked in wigs and head-dresses and spears.

"What the hell is all this?" asks the boss.

"We want to get your okay. It's costing money to keep the stuff at the studio while we're waiting for it."

Mr Brand looks over the props casually.

"It looks okay to me. Okay."

"How long do you think you'll be tied up here, boss?" asks Roy.

The boss is suddenly metamorphosed into a father and sighs heavily.

"You cannot tell about these things, Roy, and I ought to stay around for Selma's sake at such a time."

"Well, do you want me to stick around?" asks Roy.

"Thanks, Roy, but you'd better get back to the studio. I'll keep Tussler, Skinner, and Monk here. Maybe we can get some script. It's nice and quiet here. Hey, Roy, get the name of that nurse who just passed by. She looks good to me. Maybe we'll test her."

"Okay, Chief," and the stooge bounds off, followed by Rawley and Props.

"Well, Skinner, how goes the script?"

"We've broken down the story line and are all set to go into dialogue."

"That's just fine," says Mr Brand with heavy sarcasm. "You've got a story line and I've got my cameras all ready to shoot. What the hell are they going to shoot—a story line? I want dialogue. Is that too much to ask?"

"Now listen . . ." breaks in Skinner.

"Excuse me, please. Jim, have you written the announcements for the baby yet?"

"No . . . but I've a rough idea of what might do," says Jim drily.

"Okay. While we're talking story you scribble some stuff and leave a blank space for the sex of the child."

"What—is there any doubt about it?" asks Jim innocently. Mr Brand ignores him.

"Listen, Skinner. I know I'm rushing you and you haven't had much time, but they rush me all the time every day of the week. But I get my work done. Why can't you?"

"Well, look, boss. If you'd given me an experienced collaborator I would have had something. But I'm like a prep school for this guy. Not only do I have to write the story, but I have to be a teacher. He wants art and I want an Academy winner, and you can't mix oil and water."

"Look, Tussler," Mr Brand pleads. "We're in the business to make money. You've got to stop being an intellectual and we'll show you how to write motion-pictures."

"If it's all the same to you . . ." starts Mr Tussler. He is looking very fierce.

"Madge, check about the baby," breaks in Mr Brand.

I am glad of the interruption, as I have been experiencing some difficulty keeping a straight face because of Jim, who is hunched over in his chair like the statue of the Thinker with wrinkled brows, sucking a pencil, and apparently drawing upon all his genius to think up something brilliant to say about Mr Brand's baby.

"How about this, Mr Brand . . .?" he says. "A blank was born to Mrs Selma Brand, wife of the eminent producer, Sidney Brand of Super Films. Mother and child are reported resting nicely at the Vista Memorial Hospital in Hollywood. Though in the midst of an important production, *Sinners in Asylum*, which will launch Sarya Tarn, the new foreign import, Mr Brand has taken a suite at the hospital to be with his little family. . . ."

Jim delivers this straight. Mr Brand nods his head approvingly. "But, Jim," he says, "couldn't you get a little more human interest in there? Maybe about the weight of the baby and things like that. People like to read homey items. It gives Hollywood a good name too."

"Sure I can, but we'd better wait until we know exactly what happens. It might be twins. Think of the human interest you can get out of twins."

"God forbid," says Mr Brand feelingly. "Madge, maybe you'd better check again!"

I check, but there is neither a sign of a twin nor even a half a twin, and the nurse says it looks as though we have a long wait ahead of us.

"All right," says Mr Brand. "We can go to work now without interruptions. Madge, telephone the desk and tell them to hold all calls and make a record of them. Put a 'Do not disturb' sign on the door. I've got a script to write."

I do all these things and we go into conference.

Three hours and several headaches later we are arguing about the relative merits of New England or the South for the American sequences. Mr Brand holds out for New England. Social prejudices, he argues, are stronger in New England and will allow us more dramatic leeway when Tarn arrives from the jungle to meet her lover's family.

Mr Skinner stands firm on the South. We all know, he says, how the South feels about Negroes.

"We made her Spanish," reminds the boss.

Mr Tussler buries his head in his arms. He doesn't realize how vital a matter this is to decide, for it will determine whether Mr Gable is to be the scion of a proud New England family or a charming renegade of the South.

It has become so heated that Mr Skinner is minus his coat and Mr Brand minus his pyjama top, exposing a manly and hairy expanse of chest from which my girlish eyes turn in proper confusion. Jim is either sleeping or making a good play at it, for he is making some very noxious sounds.

When the 'phone rings it comes like a bombshell.

I answer. It is Bud.

"Gee, I had a terrible time getting through to you people. I've been trying to get you for ten minutes. I finally told them the studio was on fire and here I am. I want to be the first person to congratulate the boss."

"Why," I say, "because the studio is on fire?"

"No. That's a gag. It's a boy. Congratulations!"

"What?" I inquire. "Are you crazy? Did you find the key to the bar or something?"

"Listen. I'm as sober as Brand's kid. This is on the level. It's a boy!"

I turn away from the 'phone a trifle dazed.

"It's Bud, Mr Brand. He wants to congratulate you on the birth of a son!"

"What?" S. B. shoots up in his bed. "What goes on here?"

I turn back to the 'phone.

"How do you know, Bud?" I ask.

"I've been keeping a wire open to the hospital and the kid has just been born. It's all over the studio by now!"

"Check that report!" bellows Mr Brand.

I press down the key, and as I try to get Mrs Brand's room, Doctor X walks in rubbing his hands.

"Well, Sidney, it's a boy . . . someone to carry on the Brand name."

"What the hell!" explodes the boss. "Here I spend the day in the hospital and neglect my duties just to be near my wife and the studio has to tell me I'm a father. Jim! What am I paying you $250 a week for? I suppose just so that you can be scooped by a $15 a week office-boy!"

Jim comes up out of his torpor.

Automatically he intones. "A blank was born . . ."

"It's a boy!" yells Sidney.

Love,
MAGGIE

Joseph Wechsberg

FOR MANY a year (as noted elsewhere) when American writers of the picaresque or sentimental school were not contemplating the domestic scene their subject was Paris, France. True, both Harpo Marx and Alexander Woollcott had been to Moscow, but except for the heroic example of Mr Hyman Kaplan (also noted elsewhere), New York had admitted few immigrants among its humorists—unless the joke was on them.

The last two decades have seen a change. One can discern a formidable trio, urbane, casual, but exactly suited to the New York idiom, who hail (though hail is perhaps too loud a word for humour) from Austria, Italo-Roumania, and Czechoslovakia. Bemelmans, Steinberg, and Wechsberg are now firmly, even lavishly, established. Maybe it has taken a world war to widen the American horizon, but Joseph Wechsberg, at least, could claim an international training, at which his only rivals would be a composite of Benvenuto Cellini, Thor Heyerdahl, and Marco Polo.

It is simple enough to say that Wechsberg began life in Prague, held a succession of varied jobs, and eventually became an American citizen and a contributor to the *New Yorker*. Complication sets in when one begins to analyse the succession of jobs—ship's musician, croupier, beer salesman, soldier, diplomat, journalist, *claquer* at the Vienna State Opera, and other professions. As for the places in which Wechsberg lived and moved and had his being, they make the longest flying schedule of a big airline look like a suburban train journey: Vienna, Basle, Paris, India, Malaya, China, Japan, Persia, Africa, South Seas, Canada, USA, the Far North—to choose a few.

From a very small part of this emerged the reminiscences contained in *Looking for a Bluebird*. Cecil Day Lewis rightly referred to their 'Czech light-heartedness and New-Yorker edge'. They mainly concerned the adventures of a seedy ship's orchestra on second-rate French liners calling at places like Djibouti and Saigon. And just as Bemelmans takes us through to the echoing kitchens, Wechsberg beckons beyond the fading palms and peeling gilt of the orchestra platform. There, for instance, on *La Bourdonnais*, we meet Sebastiano the Sleepy Piano-Player.

⬦

THE SLEEPY PIANO-PLAYER

The laziest man I have ever known was Sebastiano, a Spanish pianist from Algeciras, who joined our four-man orchestra aboard *La Bourdonnais* for one voyage. On sailing day, Dimitrij, our regular piano-player, explained in a laconic radiogram addressed to Maurice that 'for personal reasons' he was unable to leave Paris. The personal reasons were, as we found out later, a vendeuse from the Galeries Lafayette, fourth floor, caleçons, peignoirs, ladies' underwear. Fortunately, Maurice ran into Sebastiano at the Café des Quat'z' Arts three hours before the departure of our train for Bordeaux, and hired him at once.

Maurice had worked with Sebastiano at the Rendezvous des Américains, a tiny, permanently overcrowded *boîte* in a side street off the Boulevard Raspail in Montparnasse, where the customers literally sat on one another's laps and the lights were so dim that no one was able to read the bill. In the Rendezvous, Sebastiano sat behind an upright Pleyel piano in a corner, concealed from the rest of the boîte by a heavy velvet curtain, his job being to create what Monsieur Boniface, the proprietor, referred to as *"L'atmosphère—c'est tout"*. He played soft, subdued, intimate piano music, *en sourdine*. On Saturdays he would be joined by a violinist and a 'cellist, and it was on such an occasion that he met Maurice.

The atmosphere at the Rendezvous des Américains was anything but American, Monsieur Boniface having never seen more of America than the United States Treasury building on the back of a ten-dollar bill. The bartender was from Rouen, and the headwaiter from Corsica, and Sebastiano, a pupil of Albéniz, played mostly Spanish music—Granados, de Falla, Albéniz. He was a short fellow with thin shoulders. He had beautiful dark hair, always uncombed and falling down over his forehead; prominent cheekbones, black eyes, and a colourless complexion.

Sebastiano was unbelievably lazy. He said he could sleep twenty-four hours a day for four days in a row, and I think he did not exaggerate. He liked to point out, however, that in Algeciras he was not known as an especially lazy type. "You should see my father," he once told me. "Never gets out of bed. On Easter Sunday, mother, my eleven brothers and sisters, and I have to work for an hour before we get him dressed and drag him all the way to church. There he falls asleep at once. *C'est la vie.*" Sebastiano shrugged and fell asleep himself.

Sebastiano had a tiny room at a little hotel near the Pantheon. The room was on the fourth floor and Sebastiano hated climbing up the narrow, winding stairway. Often he would sit down on the stairs between the second and third floors and fall asleep. Mademoiselle Renée, a pretty, dark-haired girl, who lived next to him, would go down and call the proprietor and his wife, and the three of them would drag Sebastiano up to his room. Renée was crazy about Sebastiano, but he was indifferent and resented her hanging up her washed panties and stockings on a string across her window. "She's frivolous," he used to say. "Most girls are. *C'est la vie.*"

He got so tired of climbing the four flights that one day he decided that from then on he would stay at the Rendezvous and sleep under the piano. He took two plush seat-covers and placed them on the floor in front of the piano. He hung his tuxedo across a chair and slipped into his pyjamas, which he had brought from his room, and slept all day long. The place was being cleaned, and Monsieur Boniface carried on long discussions with wine salesmen, and once the headwaiter from Corsica almost stabbed the cook to death with a fruit knife, but Sebastiano slept peacefully and undisturbed. Around eight-thirty that evening, the headwaiter, aided by the entire staff, started to wake up Sebastiano. By nine-thirty the pianist was ready to get up. He changed into his tuxedo, had a glass of dry sherry, and sat down at the piano. His fingers worked automatically, though his mind was still in a deep trance.

One day Sebastiano's tuxedo was stolen while he was sleeping under the piano. That night he had to play in his pyjamas. He did not mind. He hated to dress and the place was always overheated, and he was safe, anyway, behind the velvet curtain. At two in the morning two American tourists discovered him in his odd attire. They pushed him out on to the floor, where he was an instant success. Everybody agreed that wearing nothing but pyjamas was a great idea. The two Americans jumped into a taxicab, went to their hotel, and came back in their pyjamas. Everybody bought drinks for everybody else. The idea caught on, and three or four evenings later all habitués of the Rendezvous des Américains arrived at the place in their pyjamas, over which they had put on their overcoats and furs. Monsieur Boniface, a man of sound business principles, increased the prices of liquor fifty per cent and put out more lights. The son of the Corsican headwaiter was posted as guard in front of the entrance, and a small sign, MEMBERS ONLY, printed in English, was hung on the door. Only people dressed properly—that is, in pyjamas—were allowed to come in.

Sebastiano, never given to loose talk, was particularly reticent about the weeks that followed. That epoch was, he indicated, characterized by cheerful abandon and wonderfully large tips. Then the cook, who was carrying on a vendetta with the Corsican headwaiter, got fired and went to the police. The agents raided the place, and that was the end. "*C'est la vie,*" Sebastiano concluded gloomily.

The police tactfully suggested that Sebastiano find himself employment outside of France or they would have to ship him back to Algeciras. Sebastiano hopefully went to the Café Quat'z' Arts and happened on the job aboard *La Bourdonnais*.

Sebastiano began his career as ship's musician promisingly by missing the nine o'clock train which he had been ordered to take with the rest of us. He told us later that he took a taxi to the station and fell asleep. The cab-driver, unable to wake him up, took him to the nearest police station, where they managed to shake him out of his trance, but by that time our train had left. He took the midnight train and came aboard the following morning with the last group of first-class passengers. He had on his tuxedo, a yellow camel's-hair overcoat, and no hat. He had no baggage whatsoever, and looked so bored and genuinely expensive that the maître d'hôtel, who took pride in his infallible judgment of his fellow men, made his de-luxe bow and asked him for the number of his stateroom on A Deck. Two smart, tall Vassar girls, returning from their European vacation, gave him a wistful look, and a vivacious divorcée from Boston, reclining in a deck chair, put down her Michael Arlen story and stared at him in fascination.

Sebastiano was much too sleepy to return her stare. I took him down to the two connecting staterooms where the orchestra slept. Maurice started a noisy tirade. Sebastiano, his eyes half-closed, dreamily inquired which of the four berths was his. He took off his overcoat, lay down in his tuxedo, and in four seconds was sound asleep. Baggage porters bumped into the door and uttered pungent oaths, women came into our stateroom looking for their husbands, and husbands came in looking for their wives, a steward swung his bell ("Visitors ashore, all visitors ashore"), the siren wailed, but Sebastiano slept peacefully through all the excitement that preceded the sailing and we had to pour half a glass of ice water into his open mouth to get him up on deck in time for the national anthems, which were always played as the ship was being towed away from the pier. After the last note of the 'Marseillaise', he went back to bed again.

The eleven days that followed, en route to New York, were a nightmare. Sebastiano kept the three other musicians—Maurice, Lucien, who was our French first violinist, and myself, the second violin—in a perpetual state of nervous tension. We had fairly easy working hours aboard *La Bourdonnais*. There was an aperitif concert on deck, between eleven and noon; a concert in the tourist-class dining-saloon from three to four, which was merely a rehearsal for the afternoon concert in the first-class saloon from four to five; and a concert, after dinner, from eight-thirty to nine-thirty, either in the saloon or outside on deck, depending on the weather. From ten to eleven we played dance music. All in all, it was only five hours' work a day.

From the very first day, Sebastiano never showed up in time for work. As long as he was asleep in our rooms, we did not mind so much. You could always go down, pour some ice water into his mouth, and drag him upstairs. But he got tired of drinking ice water and began to hide. Twenty minutes before concert time, someone would discover that Sebastiano had vanished, and there would be a mad scramble for our piano-player. You can play without your second violinist or your 'cellist, but you have to have your pianist. The first few days we found him in fairly accessible places: lifeboats, heaps of rope on deck, the benches on the sun deck, the hospital, the tourist-class saloon. As the days went on, however, Sebastiano became more ingenious. He vanished behind stacks of breakfast-food boxes in the kitchen, in a corner of the wireless-room, in the engine-room. We had ingenious helpers in all departments of the ship, and so we always found him, though sometimes rather late.

Things started to get really tough when Sebastiano began to vanish in the staterooms of the passengers. First he vanished under the bed of Mr Wayne, a real-estate broker from New Jersey, who had Cabin No 7 and spent all his days on deck playing shuffleboard. Fortunately, the cabin steward discovered him before Mr Wayne, a tough character with a top kick's voice, could raise hell. Next, Sebastiano was found hiding in Cabin No 4, which belonged to a Mr Rhys Price, Mr Wayne's English shuffleboard partner and an outdoor man too. One evening Sebastiano went into Cabin No 35b, where the two Vassar girls lived. It was dinnertime for the first-class passengers and Sebastiano thought the young ladies were in the dining-saloon, but they were in their stateroom, and not by themselves either, and they had forgotten to lock the door. Sebastiano's face was still red as he tried to reconstruct the scene for us. "I said I was sorry, but the two men looked at me as though they were thinking of murder." He thought for a minute, and then added, "And they were, I'm sure. They had that look in their eyes. I was frightened to death. I turned around and ran. *C'est la vie, mes amis.* All you want is some sleep and what do you get? Murder."

On the day before we reached Halifax, *La Bourdonnais* ran into bad weather and many passengers became seasick. Some stayed in their cabins, but the majority spent the day on deck, lying in their chairs, their faces the colour of long-dead halibut. The deck stewards hustled back and forth, carrying trays with consommé and crackers; taking care to keep the door to the dining-room closed because the smell of food made some of the passengers wish they were dead. Mrs Sloan, the divorcée from Boston, was the sickest of all. She remained on deck until midnight, and the following day she was carried up there again early in the morning. Sebastiano had his own intelligence system among the deck personnel. That afternoon he was gone. We looked for him everywhere but did not find him.

We knocked at all the cabin doors and stammered foolish excuses when the occupants opened up and we glanced over their shoulders, trying to discover Sebastiano under a bed or behind a curtain. Some passengers got very angry, and Mr Wayne spoke his mind in unmistakable terms. We did not find Sebastiano. There was no tourist-class concert that afternoon and no concert in the first-class saloon. We were reported to the captain, and he ordered a methodical search of the steamer.

They found Sebastiano at seven o'clock. He was sleeping peacefully in Mrs Sloan's bed. He was in his underwear, his shoes were placed beside the bed, and his tuxedo was hung carefully over a chair. He explained that he did not want to get the bed dirty. The captain had us all summoned to the bridge. He was angry as never before, but Sebastiano was his old dreamy self. "It must be a sort of hypnosis, my captain," he said. "It overwhelms you. There's nothing you can do but lie down. It is stronger than you are."

Maurice said: "Maybe he has sleeping sickness without knowing it. Were you ever in the Belgian Congo, Sebastiano?" Maurice always tried to help us out when we got in a jam.

"What the hell has the Belgian Congo got to do with this?" the captain shouted. We fell silent and looked at Sebastiano, who was standing in front of the captain. The pianist's eyes were half closed and he was swaying back and forth like a tall pine in a wind. Soon, I knew, he would be asleep.

The captain stared at Sebastiano, opened his mouth, shut it again, and shrugged. "Get out of here," he said. "All of you. . . . No, wait, you!" he called Sebastiano back and ordered him to apologize to Mrs Sloan for using her bed. Sebastiano went down from the bridge to the windy, isolated place on deck where Mrs Sloan was lying in her deck chair. He kissed her hand with all his inborn Algeciras grand manner, pulled up another chair, and sat down next to her.

The following evening Sebastiano did not take his customary nap before the concert. He came down to our cabins for a moment, put on his camel's-hair overcoat and pulled up the collar, and went out again. At eight-fifteen I found him in the chair beside Mrs Sloan. I said I was sorry, but it was time for the evening concert. He nodded and helped Mrs Sloan out of her covers and gallantly escorted her to the music saloon. I walked behind them. They called one another 'Sebbie' and 'Kathie'. The lady from Boston was still pale and somewhat weak, but there was a light in her eyes as she sat down in the music saloon not far from the piano. She was a pretty woman, dark-haired and a little taller than Sebastiano. She seemed restless and excited. She watched Sebastiano. He played very well that evening. He asked Maurice to let him play a few solo numbers; he played two Chopin *études*, a piece by Debussy, and a Brahms waltz. After every piece he turned round and smiled at Mrs Sloan. It was the first time I had seen him make a movement that was not absolutely necessary. I looked at Maurice, and Maurice looked at me, and we must have had the same thought because we both forgot to close our mouths.

After the concert, Mrs Sloan invited the members of the orchestra to the bar for a drink. It was cool and she shivered, so Sebastiano volunteered to go for her mink coat. "Sebbie is such a dear boy," she said when he had gone. "He sits next to me and I talk and he just listens." She sighed and looked down at her fingernails. "My husband never did that. He never listened to me. He wasn't interested in anything I said."

There was a pause, then Maurice said, "Sebastiano is a quiet man. Very quiet."

Mrs Sloan sighed again. "He's so understanding," she said. "Doctor Wellman, my nerve specialist, always told me, 'It's so hard to find an understanding person. A man who will listen to you and——' "

Sebastiano came back with her mink coat, and she stopped in the middle of her sentence. That night, after the dance, Mrs Sloan and Sebastiano sat in the bar. She talked all the time and Sebastiano listened, motionless and rigid, like a Brahmin on the shore of the Ganges who has vowed never to move.

Sebastiano did not make the return trip with us to Europe. Two days after our arrival in New York he vanished again. We looked in all the staterooms, including the captain's, but there was no trace of our piano-player. The next morning

Maurice got a telegram from Sebastiano. Our pianist was not coming back. He was up in Boston and he had decided to stay there for good. There was one particular sentence in Sebastiano's telegram which I remember: "Boston is a nice, quiet place," he wired, "colder than Algeciras, but a good place to sleep."

Bergen Evans

THE LATE (and much-lamented) H. L. Mencken ought perhaps to have been included in this book. But re-reading his *Prejudices* and his *Defence of Women* has convinced me that Mencken will be remembered more for his opinions on debunking (he coined the phrase) than for his lighter style. The flashing phrase ('She was not so much a woman clothed, as clothing womaned') is only occasional.

I link a man like Bergen Evans with the Mencken school because his *Natural History of Nonsense* is a sustained and brilliant essay in debunking. It leaves not a rack behind of all our popular superstitions. Evans is, moreover, a scholar, and a television panel member of wit and distinction, as those who gathered at Oxford for the fiftieth Anniversary of the Rhodes Scholars will remember. *The Inside Story*, a chapter from his book, is a good example of how to be exhaustive without being exhausting.

❖

THE INSIDE STORY

Popular misconceptions concerning anatomy, physiology, and hygiene produce a great deal of confusion and discomfort. Thus about one half of all who attempt to commit suicide by shooting or stabbing themselves through the heart—from Mark Antony to Hideki Tojo—fail because they don't know where the heart is and, in consequence, shoot or stab themselves through the lung or abdomen. But it may be questioned whether such errors are, properly speaking, vulgar errors. They are often just sheer ignorance—not false deductions or gross exaggerations or the products of some system of metaphysics; and until recently most of them had, and even yet many of them have, the support of fairly eminent medical authorities.

None the less, some of them are curious enough to be worth looking at.

Hair is a great breeder of error, for some reason. Hair on the chest is thought to indicate unusual strength—probably on the assumption that a man with hair on his chest is more like a gorilla—though actually the gorilla has no hair on his chest. He has hair on his back, his shoulders, his arms, his belly, and his legs, but none on his chest.

Baldness, not hairiness, is now thought by scientists to be the true sign of masculinity. But the news hasn't yet reached the layman, or the layman's wife, and until it does the luckless man who is losing his hair must continue to lose his time, money, patience, and comfort by trying out a score of 'remedies' which he knows in advance will prove futile.

Some urge him to shave his beard closely, so that no nourishment will be diverted from his scalp. Others would have him clip his hair short, so that what nourishment there is will be concentrated. Barbers often advise singeing the ends of the hairs after a haircut 'to keep in the vital fluid'. Some reproach him for having 'rotted' his hair by wetting it to make it lie down. Some are sure that his hat-band has been too tight. And some think that he has offended a celestial Emily Post by wearing his hat indoors. All are wrong (with the possible exception of the last, whose contention can't be disproved), but they are not without their usefulness. Among them they usually manage to make the wretched man thoroughly happy when he has finally gone completely bald and so is no longer an object of their solicitude.

Commonest of all fictions about the hair is that as a result of some 'harrowing' experience it may turn white overnight. The myth in its full classic splendour is given by Ludwig Bemelmans—though more, one suspects, as a contribution to humour than to physiology. In *My War with the United States* he tells the story of a tug that had drifted by mischance to the top of Niagara Falls and was held from plunging over only by a small boulder upon which it had grounded. All one foggy night the Police and Fire departments of Buffalo laboured in the rescue, while the tug scraped over the rock inch by inch; and when in the morning the members of the crew were finally taken off, only a second before the vessel was hurled into the abyss, every hair of every man 'had turned white from horror'.

Perhaps the night air has something to do with it; hair never seems to turn white over day. Or maybe it is easier to misplace the bottle of hair dye in the dark, though such conjectures seem very flippant when one considers the innumerable 'authentic' instances that have been reported in the medical journals. Gould and Pyle have made an impressive collection of them. One is of a woodsman who awakened to find a grizzly bear standing over him and was grizzled instantly. Another is of a gambler who placed his all on the turn of a card and awoke next morn to find himself a sadder, whiter man. Most gruesome of all is the account they quote 'of hair suddenly turning grey after death'. There's a respect 'to make calamity of so long life'.

This belief, like the head-hiding ostrich, lives on because it is so useful. It is a hall-mark of horror. It saves endless description. Don't labour to be frightful, just have someone's hair turn white overnight.

The hard-pressed editors of *Time*, for instance, find it exceedingly serviceable. They assure us that Ernie Pyle's hair turned 'grey' during the African campaign, while Air Marshal Coningham's (perhaps in deference to his rank) turned 'silver grey'. Mr C. Yates McDaniel, after watching 'the collapse at Singapore at close hand', had turned 'almost white', though it was confessed that the observation of earlier horrors up the Yangtze had earned him 'many a thread of silver to begin with'. As the allies advanced towards the Rhine, Pierre Laval, cowering in Berlin, was rumoured to be 'turning white', and three years in Sing Sing was alleged to have had the same effect on Jimmie Hines.

Many of the stories carry their own refutation, or at least a suggestion of a more plausible explanation. Thus the very picture of Mr McDaniel which *Time*, with admirable candour, ran with the story showed that at the time of going to press he still had a reserve of pigmentation to be lost in future horrors, and the picture of Air Marshal Coningham on the cover of the issue that described him showed only a touch of greyness at the temples. Pierre Laval was sixty-one at the time of his alleged transformation and Jimmie Hines was sixty-seven —ages at which saints have been known to acquire what, in their cases, is described as a 'halo' or 'aureole' of white hair. And if M. Laval's bleaching was due, as was implied, to fear for his own safety, one wonders why it had not taken place three years earlier, when there were a number of attempts to assassinate him.

But great as is the concern about hair, it is secondary, as a cause of both interest and error, to the concern about food. Religion, habit, custom, squeamishness, fads, fancies, all affect our ideas of what is and what is not fit to eat, and almost all of them today have 'scientific' sanction.

The average man regards his own diet as sensible and all deviations from it as finicky or loathsome. When the normal American, for instance, reads that Mexicans eat fried worms, that Indians eat dogs and monkeys, that Africans eat grasshoppers, and that the Chinese and many Europeans eat coagulated blood, he simply retches and thanks God for the good old USA, where wholesome food comes in bright cans and crisp boxes. As for the delicacies of antiquity—Heliogabalus' combs and wattles of cocks, Maecenas' asses flesh, and Trimalchio's 'dugs of pregnant sow'—it is probably just as well for his digestion that he never even heard of them.

Yet among his own simple viands are several that other people would regard with abhorrence. A third of mankind would rather die than touch his morning bacon. Biologically considered, his glass of milk is grossly indecent, and, even among those who accept milk as edible, millions prefer the milk of horses. His juicy steak would be an abomination to hundreds of millions, and many more would gladly exchange it, as a mere piece of muscle, for the liver, stomach, or heart of the same animal.

The fairly limited number of foods that most people commonly permit themselves is still further limited, in practice, by the widespread belief that certain foods that are good in themselves are bad when mixed. Cucumbers and ice-cream were formerly thought to give the eater cholera, possibly because of some false analogy between their coldness and the subnormal temperature that characterizes that disease. Pickles-and-milk and fish-and-celery were, and by many still are, regarded as dangerous combinations. A whole cult gravitates around the delusion that proteins and starches should not be eaten at the same meal, despite the fact that there is some protein in all food and that milk, nature's basic food, contains proteins and carbohydrates.

Other popular delusions about the digestive organs and

their functionings are that fish is good for brain workers, that unusual hunger indicates a tapeworm, that a sudden fright cures hiccups, and that constipation causes 'auto-intoxication'.

The brain contains phosphorus and so does fish, but the phosphorus in the brain does not have to be continually replenished, and even if it did there is no proof that it would be obtained any more easily from fish than from many other foods. The belief may possibly owe something to an association of a fish diet and the clergy through the centuries during which the clergy had a monopoly of intellectual work.

The common theory of the tapeworm is that it eats so much of its victim's food that he is eternally hungry. Actually, however, a tapeworm eats very little and manifests its presence by no symptoms whatever—although many people are nauseated when they know they have one. Morbid hunger is more likely to be a symptom of diabetes.

Hiccups are spasms of the diaphragm, variously attributed to indigestion, gas on the stomach or in the intestines, alcohol, heart disease, pregnancy, pneumonia, certain nervous afflictions, and inflammation of the diaphragm itself. Extreme fright has been said to cause abortions, and so it might end one of the causes, but the others are not amenable to such a remedy. The belief, however, has its devotees, and almost a martyr in John Mytton of Halston, who set fire to his own nightshirt to effect a cure.

The annoying thing is that hiccups usually die down soon of their own accord, so that the sufferer often has to endure the triumphant 'I told you so' of the egregious ass who frightened him as well as the exasperation of the hiccups themselves.

Auto-intoxication is one of the great modern bugaboos. The theory of it, expounded over the radio with fulsome delicacy, is that the body absorbs from the clogged intestines poisons that would normally have been excreted. Many physiologists, on the other hand, are of the exact contrary opinion. They hold that poisoning from the large intestine is more likely when laxatives have moved the contents of the small intestine too quickly. The food and moisture content of the colon are then abnormally high and hence bacteria are enabled to grow with rapidity.

One of the commonest illusions concerning diet is that certain foods have special properties to stimulate sexual desire.

But aside from cantharides, which act as a vesicant and arouse sensations far too painful to be regarded as amorous by any but the morbid, it may be doubted if there is such a thing as a genuine aphrodisiac. Alcohol, it is true, often has the effect of one; but it operates not so much by increasing thoughts of love as by lessening thoughts of consequences.

Many foods, however, have been claimed to be aphrodisiacs. Antiquity favours onions, though our more squeamish times would probably regard them as definitely inhibitory. The Elizabethans ascribed the power to so many articles of diet that one suspects that in that virile but undernourished age all anyone needed was a square meal. They set especial store by potatoes, eryngoes, and tobacco, and thought so well of prunes, in this respect, that they served them as free lunches in their brothels. Modern lore follows Casanova's prescription of oysters but places equal faith in raw eggs, which are thought to be great strengtheners of virility as well.

Even more widespread is the belief that saltpetre is an anti-aphrodisiac and is secretly introduced into the food at colleges, prisons, and other places where amorous impulses are thought to have ungovernable force. It is safe to say that there is not a boys' school or an army camp in the country in which this myth is not entrenched. Yet as far as the camps go, physical exhaustion obviates any need for sedatives; and as far as the schools go, if saltpetre *is* put into the food, the prevailing temper of the young gentlemen refutes its alleged effects.

(No discussion of vulgar errors could touch on oysters without mentioning the belief that they are poisonous in the months whose names do not have an *r* in them. Before the development of refrigerated transport this belief may have had some foundation in the fact that the months without an *r* are summer months when sea food that had to be shipped inland was particularly likely to spoil. Furthermore, the summer is the spawning season of oysters, and during this season they often taste flat. But there is nothing poisonous about them.)

The belief in aphrodisiacs may be based on an unconscious desire to gratify forbidden impulses without having to accept the moral responsibility for doing so. There is a similar fascination, seemingly, in the thought of all drugs. The Press plays them up sensationally and standardizes certain errors or exaggerations.

A few years ago the editors of half the popular magazines in America became addicted to marihuana—as a subject for copy —and sent their own and their magazines' circulation soaring with delicious dreams of high-school girls abandoning themselves to orgies under the influence of this subtle drug. 'Reefers' were identified as the root of half the evil then extant. The *Readers Digest* felt that the number of 'murders, suicides, robberies, and maniacal deeds' committed every year by children under the influence of marihuana could 'only be conjectured'.

They and their readers may be interested in one conjecture, that of Dr Le Moyne Synder, Medicolegal Director of the Michigan State Police. His conjecture at least for the State of Michigan during the years when all such matters would have come to his attention: none. And his belief that it is 'questionable' whether or not a true addiction to the drug is often developed is supported by a study of the problem made by a special committee of doctors in New York City—though it should be stated that the conclusions of this committee were severely condemned in an editorial in the *Journal of the American Medical Association*. Still, the very existence of such writings and opinions shows that the case is not so closed as laymen might assume.

There are a number of delusions concerning the milder drugs and poisons to which the public *is* addicted. Tea is commonly thought to be more healthful than coffee, though both contain approximately the same amount of caffeine, and smoking is thought to relieve tension and alcohol to act as a stimulant.

Tobacco acts first as an excitant and then as a depressant. Irritability, restlessness, impaired memory, depression of spirits, insomnia, headache, and fatigue have all been demonstrated to be the physical consequences of excessive smoking. Even two cigarettes can produce a measurable dulling of sensitivity and increase of tremor.

The immediate effect of alcohol is stimulating, but the general effect is sedative. The nervous system is depressed and drowsiness ensues. It seems stimulating only because the first manifestation of its depressive action is a lowering of inhibitions, with a consequent feeling of release.

But it must be added that alcohol is not quite the villain,

either, that some would have us think. Drs Haggard and Jellinek, of the Yale University School of Medicine, after an exhaustive study have come to the conclusion that the ascription of stomach ulcers, arterio-sclerosis, kidney diseases, cancer, and especially cirrhosis of the liver to alcoholism as the due penalties of wickedness is unjustified. It is their opinion that the diseases of chronic alcoholism 'are essentially nutritional disturbances'. They grant that there is an abnormally high incidence of cirrhosis of the liver among heavy drinkers, but they point out that the disease also occurs among non-drinkers and that there is 'as yet no certain knowledge' of its cause in either group. They feel that alcohol is bad for anyone who has an ulcer, but they do not believe that alcohol alone would cause an ulcer, and they found less hardening of the arteries and less cancer among chronic alcoholics than among the general population of the same age. Perhaps there are, as Rabelais said, more old drunkards than old doctors.

Some of the old drunkards might attribute their longevity to the fact that they had so much alcohol in their blood that they were immune from infection, for it is widely believed that liquor is antiseptic and that the blood absorbs it in full strength. Both beliefs are illusory: alcohol cannot be drunk or absorbed into the bloodstream in any concentration strong enough to kill germs.

In a confused way, some such idea must be behind the belief that whisky is good for a snakebite, though actually, because it increases circulation and so spreads the venom more rapidly through the system, it is bad. Some, by extension, seem to think that 'alcohol in the blood' is an antidote for any poison, and we read, in the *New Yorker*, of a man who was bitten by a black widow but who was 'fortunately an alcoholic' and so 'threw off with ease a dose of venom that would probably have destroyed an abstemious man'.

The belief that a little oil taken before drinking will prevent drunkenness is very old. Plutarch had it from Claudius, his physician. In those days it was oil of bitter almonds; now it is olive oil or mineral oil, though some recommend cream. One modern theory is that the oil spreads an impenetrable film over the wall of the stomach—though if this were so, any taken with any meal would stop all digestion. The ancient theory was that oil would spread a film over the surface of the alcohol and so prevent the fumes from rising into the 'limbeck' of the brain.

Next to digestive and reproductive systems, the respiratory system seems the object of the greatest common concern and confusion. Most of the illusions are grouped around the common cold, which the layman usually ascribes to exposure to a low temperature. The experts, however, say that colds are caused by a 'filterable virus' plus the action of variable factors, including chilling. Which being interpreted means that colds are caused by whatever it is that causes colds.

Except in so far as it conduces to avoiding infection, the out-of-doors life, sleeping on porches, and so on, does nothing to 'build up resistance' to colds. A Gallup poll showed that farmers, as a group, 'have slightly more colds than other groups in the population', and one of the most striking features of the 'flu epidemic of 1917–18 was the high mortality among the young and healthy.

Cold baths are more a matter of pride than of prophylaxis. They may be refreshing to the person who takes them, but they are tiring to those who have to hear him tell about them. Apart from cleanliness, hot or cold baths do not improve the health. More people have died in bathtubs than ever lived in them.

One of the most pathetic fallacies of sufferers from severe respiratory diseases is the widespread belief that a dry climate will 'dry up' the infection. Thousands of the tuberculous believe that if they could only get to Arizona or the Sahara their infection would magically disappear. But such hopes are doomed to disappointment. The air of the average house or flat is often drier than that of any desert, but it makes no difference, for our bodies have an elaborate mechanism to ensure that the humidity of all air entering the lungs is close to the saturation point. If a change of climate has a beneficial effect, it is through its effect on the general health or because a change of environment often makes a change of living habits easier.

The remedies proposed for the common cold are as numerable as they are futile. Some urge whisky, some urge lemon juice, and some a mixture of the two. 'Alkalinizing' has all the attraction of mystery and meaninglessness, and hundreds of tons of bicarbonate of soda are poured annually down a million gullets, though, fortunately for the possessors of the gullets, no amount of bicarbonate or any other substance will alkalinize the system. Honey and pine preparations, possibly because they suggest the great out of doors, have their devotees.

The injunction to 'Feed a cold and starve a fever' leads some to eat heavily when they have a cold and others to eat sparingly. The first regard the proverb as a direct prescription, but the second feel that its true meaning is '*If* you feed a cold, you will have to starve a fever later'. Both are wrong. A person with a cold requires no more food than he does in normal health, but illnesses accompanied by fever require extra food to build up wasted tissue.

Manufacturers of cosmetics have done much to strengthen the belief that we breathe through our skins, though if we did we would be suffocated by most of their products. Some oxygen is taken in through the skin and some carbon dioxide given off, but the quantity is negligible and the respiration probably goes no farther than the skin itself. There are stories of persons who have 'smothered' as a result of having their skins gilded or varnished, but hundreds have been tarred and feathered and thousands—in the war—coated with oil (which would have the same effect) without fatal consequences. A quaint old New England belief, related to this, was that if you held your breath the pores would be closed, so that a bee or a wasp could not get his sting in and, after several vain attempts, would finally go away disgusted.

There is something about human beings when they are trying out a health theory that would make almost anyone go away disgusted.

Richard Bissell

After graduation from Harvard with a Bachelor of Science degree in 1936, Richard Pike Bissell sailed as an ordinary seaman on an American Export Line to the Azores, Marseilles, Naples, Genoa, Livorno, and other Mediterranean ports. In 1938 he shipped with the Federal Barge Lines from St Louis to St Paul, and in 1942 he went to work for the Central Barge Company of Chicago as deckhand and mate on the Illinois River. He retired from the river and became secretary-treasurer of a clothes company which makes men's pyjamas, shirts, and sportswear. He was also factory-superintendent and stylist for the company.

He is married and has four children. The family moved from their houseboat in Iowa to Long Island Sound during the Broadway success of 'The Pajama Game' as a musical. Richard Bissell is now working on a book about show-business as a result of his experience in the staging of the play; his other novels, *A Stretch on the River* and *High Water*, are both about towboats.

⊷

THE PAJAMA GAME

A Country Merchant sometimes known as the
Man behind the Face, was sitting in his
Prunery one Day when a Drummer came in to
Sell him a lot of Goods he didn't need.

(GEORGE ADE)

The attempt on the part of Sleep Tite Top Management to fire Catherine Williams was one of the most colossal fizzles in the history of American industry. Also the shortest.

First I tore up the note in a fine frenzy and just sat cussing for about five minutes and raising hell with the universe.

"And Williams of all people," said Mabel. "Oh, my god."

"Well, this is where the poor but honest young foreman

204

goes into the big boss's office and tells him off," I said. "I don't have to take this kind of . . ."

"Oh, my god," Mabel said. "Where are my Tums at? What a day!"

I combed my hair and took the elevator down to the main office and walked down through the office while the stenos stared at me and lost a couple of beats in their gum symphony and I walked right into Hasler's office. He was on the telephone, so I backed out the door to wait, but not before I heard him saying:

". . . and every red-blooded believer in the free enterprise system should sit down and write Hickenlooper and tell him . . ."

I stood outside and the elevator boy went by and winked at me. First sign of life I ever saw out of him. I felt like a sap, standing there outside the principal's office, but it wasn't for long. Hasler hollered, "Come on in, Sorokin, come on in."

His office looked like the wealthy railroad president's office in one of the 1910 silent movies where the hero shoots his cuffs and rolls his eyeballs almost into the camera. It was all there, the black-oak trim, the black-oak chairs, the black-oak hatrack, the black-oak desk, the wire letter-basket, the chromo of the Falls of the Yellowstone, the steel engraving of General U. S. Grant, the photo of the Board of Directors in high collars, and even a nickel-plated stand-up telephone.

"I got your note about Williams," I said.

"Naturally. Well, what about it?" he said, arranging his jaw into 'fighter' position. "Did you can her yet?"

"Look, Mr Hasler," I said. "We're sitting on a keg of gunpowder up there. The help is sore about no wage increase, so they started this slowdown to bring the thing to a head. If we fire Williams we'll play right into their hands. They'll . . ."

"Nonsense," he said. "The girl's a trouble-maker. Probably all full of socialistic crazy idea. She's . . ."

"They'll claim she was fired without cause and by tomorrow morning we'll have a strike. Not a machine will sew a stitch tomorrow. The shipping room will have to close down and somebody will have to . . ."

"No strike. I won't permit a strike on these premises. I . . ."

". . . and somebody will have to write *our customers and tell them they are not going to get their pajamas for the holiday trade*," I said. I was talking plainer than I ever had with Hasler, but I was through playing around—I figured if he gives the air so much the better, let the silly bastard fire me and I'd go smell the breezes off Lake Michigan again.

"Never mind about the customers," he said. "Your job is the factory," he jabbed his finger at me.

"And then at the end of the year," I said—I was getting mighty hot and unattractively red in the face—"then at the end of the year somebody will have to explain to the stockholders how come we had a strike and lost half our holiday business and how come no dividends."

He slowly puffed up like an insulted toad at this—he was so flabbergasted he couldn't say a word, he just stared at me—'balefully', what I mean.

"All right then," he said, finally, like somebody had stuck a pin in him and he was slowly deflating. "You're supposed to know labour relations." He had a mighty funny look on his face, like he was getting some sense for a change.

One of the office girls came and stuck her head around the corner of the door. "Excuse me," she says in her usual flat voice, "but can you sign these cheques now, Mr Hasler? Mr O'Hara is out and won't be back."

She gave him the cheques and he signed them and all you could hear was the scratching of his old stub pen, and I gazed innocently out of the window at the dirty sky that looked like the sun had gone on a sympathy strike with the Sleep Tite girls. Then I looked at General Grant and then at the girl and by god *she* winked at me. She was one of these fresh squirts from the Business College that had been here just long enough to know I was new and a Big City Boy and that Hasler was some kind of laff, so she winked. A winking girl is quite a novelty actually. I began to feel a little more confidence in my future in the garment trade.

"You claim they *want* us to discharge this Williams girl?" Hasler said when the winker had departed for the accounting dept. The idea seemed to surprise him. He looked puzzled, like a dribble-glass victim.

"Why sure they do, Mr Hasler," I said, switching to a more informal, practically humble tone (after the way I'd been talking).

206

"Maybe you're right," he said, swivelling around in his old slatback chair with the shiny black leather seat.

"And Rubinstein is coming next week," I said. "We've got to face this thing sometime."

"No wage increase!" he shouted all of a sudden, and slammed his fist down among the untidy papers on the black-oak 1911 desk. "You don't have to fire Williams, maybe, but no increase! We're going to fight this thing, Sorokin!"

Let him find out for himself. Let him and Henry B. Walthall and Francis X. Bushman have a conference and plan a course of action to take against the Associated Garment Workers, Local 561.

"Rubinstein will be here Monday am," I said.

"Rubinstein," he said. "A very tricky fellow. Very clever fellow that one."

"I got Murdock's note about collars," I said. "We'll check those patterns."

"Do you know Rubinstein, Sorokin?"

"Sure, I know him."

"What about him?"

"He's smart. That's all I know. And he can get tough, so I hear."

"Did you see Fulton Lewis Jr last night?" Hasler said. "It seems there's this bill to make Labour Unions unconstitutional and Fulton Lewis says . . ."

"My radio is busted," I said.

I went back to the factory.

"Well, everything is gonna be jake," I said, sitting down at my desk. "Everything is going to be fine."

"Thank the lord for that, anyways," Mabel said. "I ate three Tums since you went down to the office, I was that worried. What happened?"

"Well, it seems there is this bill in Congress, or maybe it isn't quite there yet, but anyway it is going to make Labour Unions unconstitutional. As soon as it becomes Law, why we are going to can Williams and cut the minimum wage to 25 cents an hour. So you can see everything is all OK, and nothing to worry about. Hasler is not so dumb as he looks, see?"

"Well, I am relieved to see you in a joking mood again," she said. "But what happened?"

So I told her what happened, including the winking office girl, and she said she was glad I had made a good impression and not got mad at Mr Hasler because she was getting used to having me around and a few jokes once in a while and all that and she would not like to of seen me get fired just yet.

"Here's your copy of the Sleep Tite *Flash*," she added. "Why don't you just set down, and for once I'll close the door and you relax a little and read the *Flash* and relax."

She closed the door and set my mimeographed copy of the Sleep Tite *Flash* on the desk in front of me.

"By the way, what did he say about that Murdock letter and them terrible collars?" she said, working the slats on the Venetian blind too far one way, then too far the other way.

"I mentioned it, but he said nothing. I believe he had forgotten all about it already," I said.

"Do you want a piece of divinity fudge?" Mabel said. "It come from the Lutheran Church social."

"OK give me some Lutheran fudge," I said.

'ARE YOU CASHING IN ON SPOT BUSINESS ? ? ? ?' the Sleep Tite *Flash* said:

We are getting some swell immediate orders from some of you boys who are still out plugging the Spring Line. Here's some honeys that whizzed into our midst this week, *and were shipped out* (most of them) THE SAME DAY:

Great Bend, Montana	$110
Mt Ayr, Iowa	60
Ft Scott, Kan.	170
Casper, Wyoming	50
Napoleon, Ohio	230
(Nice going, Ed Taylor!)	
Eugene, Oregon	140
Niles, Mich.	195
Newburyport, Mass	85

These little *additional* orders pay the same commission, boys, so get in there and DIG for the SPOT ORDER, when you are selling the beautiful Spring Line of Sleep Tite, the line of irresistible Sales Appeal for Men who *Care* at Bedtime!

JACK ROLAND does it AGAIN.

Gather round, gentlemen, and you shall hear a wondrous tale to out hearts so dear, a tale of selling skill, sagacity, and Sleep Tite Pluck and Determination. To wit as follows:

Jack Roland speaking:

'Ever since I took over this territory have been trying to land Marx and Klein, the biggest department store and biggest volume outlet in paj. in the whole territory. Of course we are a little high for them with our E-Z drawstring and other features and they have been featuring some eastern kike paj. out of Baltimore or Phily or some place and I could never get Mr Jacobs the buyer even over the sample room. He used for an excuse that he did not like our four-piece crotch construction. Anyway the store was very busy they are doing a nice fall business and store decorated very beautiful and really pulling in customers so I figured if I could never intice him to sample rm. in normal times I will never succeed now with the rush on. However when I entered the furnishings Mr Jacobs was very friendly and when I asked him to come over to sample rm. instead of giving me the brush off he says he can get away at 3 pm. Upshot of it was I sold him a bill (enclosed) of over $1000.00 for spring. This was all due to my going in the store whereas I was so discouraged over this acct. I almost never even went in to see Jacobs at all. The reason for it was he says he has changed his mind about our four-piece crotch and is going to give it a whirl.'

That's what we call 'sticking' until it hurts. And does it pay off! Ask Jack Roland!

But to get away from the serious side of things for a moment...

"How about another piece of divinity?" Mabel said.
"OK," I said.

... away from the serious side of things for a moment, we modern Sales Engineers with our scientific and streamline methods of selling may tend to look with a smile or perhaps even a sneer at the old-fashioned drummer with his hearty handclasp, but maybe we with all our technical knowledge are lacking something these old-timers had in abundance, namely a SENSE OF HUMOUR!

Sometimes there are times in every salesman's career when a grin or a hearty laugh will win the day. Here's one we read someplace the other day which illustrates our point:

Take the case of a young salesman who had been trying for days to see a certain very hard-boiled executive. This executive was a tyrant, an old curmudgeon who even the old experienced salesmen found a vexatious problem.

Finally the young salesman gained admittance to 'the Lion's Den' and walked in, striving with all his might to look cool, composed and forceful.

Just then the salesman stepped on a freshly waxed spot on the floor, both feet shot out, and he found himself sprawled on the floor. There was nothing in his sales manual to cover a situation like this, so he cast technique to the four winds and simply laughed. The executive was but a breath behind him. When their mirth subsided they visited, and out of this visit grew an order running into hundreds of dollars.

See What We Mean? How's *your* sense of humour? There's a lot of truth in that story if you just think it over, don't you agree?

"Say, Mabel," I said. "How long is it since this floor was waxed?"

"Why, only last week. What's the matter with it?"

"Oh, nothing."

"Doesn't it look all right?"

"Yeah, it looks OK," I said.

For your information we have booked the BIGGEST PAJAMA BUSINESS in our history dating back to 1912. Our factory is working at top speed to assure all loyal customers and New Accounts that their gloriously-styled Sleep Tite pajamas will be shipped promptly for the Holiday Trade. From the cutting-room, through the sewing floors and down to inspection, each Sleep Tite employee is literally 'knocking himself out' to boost production and deliver the goods *where* it's wanted, *when* it's wanted.

"Haha," I said. "Some humorist is evidently writing this bulletin now."

"What's the matter?" Mabel said.

"Nothing," I said. "Give me another hunk of divine fudge."

Elsa Maxwell

THE SURPRISING thing about 'the most fabulous hostess of all time' is that so far she has only written one book, *I Married the World*. But that marriage has been a busy one, ever since Miss Maxwell, at the age of twelve, vowed she would give wonderful parties when she grew up.

The trouble is, Elsa never grew up. Her gatherings had, and still have, the inconsequent hilarity and occasional unkindness of a children's party. The 'hostess with the mostest' (and Miss Maxwell deserves the title more than the original inspirer of *Call Me Madam*) never pays the bill, unless the money has casually come her way, and is expendable. She lives on air: some would say hot air, since she never ceases her lively, spicy comments on reigning café society.

When she appeared on television recently in London, Miss Maxwell enthralled the studio with her outrageous comments and dazzled it with a Dessès dress which made her look like an oriental tea-cosy. I never needed to ask her for a script, but from the recording I have treasured her concluding, spontaneous remarks. "My father taught me four rules of life. One, never be afraid of *They*—by They I mean public opinion. Two, never collect inanimate objects, or in the end they will possess you, and you will lose your freedom. Three, take important things lightly and light things seriously. Four, always laugh at yourself before anyone else can. If you can abide by these four—the world is yours. I ought to know," she concluded, "I married it!"

⊰⊱

I MARRIED THE WORLD

Ever since the newspapers began identifying me as the Number 1 party-giver back in the 1930s I have been receiving on the average 300 letters a month asking how I do it. Most of the letters are tinged with overtones of despair. Parents want to know how they can create a social atmosphere at home that will keep their children out of night clubs. Wives beg for suggestions that will rouse lethargic husbands out of the doldrums or, more urgently, curb their explorations in more inviting pastures. The most pathetic letters come from girls who have no social life and wonder wistfully how they can meet young men.

The letters are depressing because they imply that I have a mysterious formula which, if divulged, will guarantee automatically the success of a party. That's utter nonsense, of course. The principal element of a party is perfectly obvious. Congenial, stimulating people make good parties. If guests are provocative or amusing conversationalists, a hostess merely has to bring them together for an enjoyable evening. Since conversation is a dying art, though, it usually is necessary to have in reserve a novel idea that will prop up a sagging party. If I have any formula it is nothing more than a little originality.

Virtually every woman who asks for advice makes the superfluous point of reminding me that her limited budget does not permit elaborate entertainment. As though I didn't know. I wasn't trying to contrive an epigram in the last chapter when I wrote that the best parties are given by people who can't afford them. Sure, my most publicized affairs are fancy galas and costume balls. But in the last thirty years I've given a thousand small, intimate parties that were just as much fun and within the reach of anyone's pocket-book.

Actually, I learnt to give parties in London. When I came over after the First World War, the late Mrs Benjamin Guinness, who was living in Carlton House Terrace, allowed me to move in with a piano to a small mews house she possessed. In the offing was a charity concert she was organizing in her house which Queen Mary, the Queen of Spain, Princess Marie Louise, and her sister, Princess Helena Victoria, had promised to attend.

She had asked me to rustle round and do what I could to help and I had enlisted the services of Margaret Namara, the wife of Guy Bolton, the writer of musical comedies. I also roped in a young tenor whom I'd met in America and believed had a great future, Lauritz Melchior. I asked him to sing a song of mine for which I would play the accompaniment.

As I was a little shaky on royal procedure in those days I

asked Mrs Guinness if I were expected to acknowledge the Queen's presence in any way.

"Yes," she said. "As you pass in front of Her Majesty, who will be sitting a little in front of the rest of the audience, you must curtsy on your way to the concert platform and again on your return."

At that time I was much heavier than I am now—don't say it's not possible, I was!—and dipping to the ground was no easy assignment; however all went well on the outward journey and I sank and rose like a buoy on a swell. Our contribution was a success, and the Queen applauded warmly, but on making my second curtsy on our return I passed too near the Queen, my foot slipped on the polished parquet and my two hundred pounds landed not at Her Majesty's feet but on them. If it was hideously embarrassing for me, it must have been extremely painful for her. It was then I appreciated her perfect dignity and composure confronted with a somewhat ridiculous situation. For without the slightest change of expression Her Majesty leaned down and helped me to my feet as though it were the most natural thing in the world and quite an accepted custom for ladies to come crashing down on her feet.

My face as red as peony, I wanted to crawl into the woodwork and die of shame, but Queen Mary further saved my utter mortification by breaking the ghastly silence and covering up my retreat by complimenting Melchior on his singing. Only recently the Queen of Spain recalled the incident when I met her in Rome. It was while talking with her and the Princess Helena Victoria after the concert that I suddenly found myself saying to the Princess, "But, Ma'am, why don't you come to a party in our little mews house?"

"I'd love to," she said. "When will it be?"

And at once I had to cudgel my brains to fix a date. This agreed upon, I realized that the Princess would have to be appropriately escorted.

"Ma'am," I said, "you'll need a gentleman-in-waiting." Lord Alington—'Naps'—a gay young friend of mine, was standing near and I suggested him.

"Certainly," she agreed. "Napier, you will be my gentleman-in-waiting."

'Naps' bowed low. "I am honoured, Ma'am," he replied.

Princess Helena Victoria, the great Victoria's grand-daughter, was a charming, amusing, intelligent woman, but I had to guard against the fact that a 'Royal' being present might impose a certain formality on the party. The atmosphere had to be gay and informal or the Princess would be as bored as the rest. Whom to get to entertain her? Dickie Gordon and I got busy and went to see our new friend, Noël Coward, in Ebury Street, where his mother let rooms to 'gentlemen'. I said, "Noël, you've got to help us out." And he did.

The seating arrangements may not have been royal, but they were comfortable. What we lacked in chairs we made up in cushions on the floor. Olivier of the Ritz might have raised a disapproving eye at our supper buffet, but at least it was adequate if hardly a gargantuan repast. There were sausages, sandwiches, coffee, and beer. Total cost, 13s. 6d.

Noël Coward played and sang, Ivor Novello played and sang, so did I, and Gertrude Lawrence's impish, lyrical voice enchanted us all. I know we included an imitation of French and Italian opera in which I think nearly everybody joined, Lady Diana Cooper, Viola Tree, Lois Sturt, Lord Alington's volcanic sister, Sir Harry and Lady Mainwaring, and a faun-like young man whose drawings were just beginning to attract a little attention—Oliver Messel. That lovely, blue-eyed Gaiety girl, Denise Orme, then Lady Churston and now the Duchess of Leinster, hardly left the piano, either singing with us or alone, beseeching whoever was at the keys to play this or that but never facing towards the room until Princess Helena Victoria called to her, "If you'd only turn round we could hear you so much better." At which she did. I think the Princess went home at four and I think I could claim that Elsa Maxwell's No 1 London party was a success. Because I was pretty sure everybody had enjoyed themselves, including the hostess.

It was in London some three years earlier with Lady Diana Cooper, Lois Sturt, Lord Alington, Lord Pembroke, the late Freddie Guest, and the Hon. Freddie Cripps, the redoubtable Sir Stafford's brother, that I was the ring-leader in an escapade that really makes me wince to think about. I mean it was really rather foolhardy, and but for the British sense of humour which is never far from the surface under any circumstances, we might have been caught up in an ugly scene. It was the first Three Arts Ball at Covent Garden in 1919 after the war.

"Why don't we go to the ball dressed up as a pre-war German brass band?" I suggested. No sooner said than done. We hired uniforms, got hold of a weird collection of papier-mâché instruments that nevertheless all produced a variety of comb-and-paper noises, and we industriously practised a number of tunes, including the then famous, '*Ach! du liebe Augustine!*' I decided to wear a blonde wig and a wispy walrus moustache in order to lead the band as Kapellmeister. Before the ball we dined at the Ivy Restaurant, which had just entered on its long career of popularity, and afterwards changed there into our costumes and makeup. Only Lady Diana had decided not to be a bandsman; she had dressed up as a peasant, a refugee from a devastated area. She still looked lovely.

Out from the Ivy we marched down Long Acre to Covent Garden with trombones, trumpets, and tubas blaring and passers-by eyeing us curiously. On arrival at Covent Garden the attendants looked at us with more than curiosity, in fact they obviously thought there might be trouble. "Go in at your own risk," they said.

In we went, myself leading the way, the band booming behind me, 'Ach! du liebe Augustine!' Not a pre-eminently welcome tune with the war only a few months over. Hardly had we got on to the floor than there was pandemonium. There were hoots, yells, and catcalls. I thought it was touch and go whether the dancers were going to tear us to pieces or join in our prank. Suddenly there was a roar of cheers and everyone in the whole vast ballroom started to follow us round the floor. The joke had been appreciated, we were the success of the ball.

But that was not enough for me, I thought we should attempt new fields to conquer. I remembered that General 'Tom' Bridges and his wife, Lady Bridges, were giving a dinner-party for Dame Nellie Melba and Sir John Sargent, the famous painter. "Let's go on there," I suggested, "and stage a repeat performance."

So off we went and under their windows started to serenade the party by marching up and down and kicking up the most frightful din on our papier-mâché trumpets. Up went the windows and Tom Bridges began to throw pennies down at us; then we revealed who we were, at which Sargent roared with delight and even Dame Nellie Melba requested an encore. By now we decided we were really well worth hearing and that the one place that would be delighted to receive us was the Embassy Club in Bond Street. The Embassy at that time was run by the adroit and admirable Luigi, who could handle princes and *poules*—*du premier rang, bien entendu*—with consummate skill and charm. Evening dress was then *de rigueur* at dinner and supper, though I once saw one man there at night in a frock-coat. It was Sir Austen Chamberlain, then Chancellor of the Exchequer. His hostess was my implacable foe, Lady Cunard.

Though we were in anything but evening dress, and Lady Diana was almost in rags and tatters, Luigi was so delighted with our appearance that he made us take the place of the band! Triumph was ours. And Lady Oxford and Asquith left her table and insisted on joining us. I remember we finished the evening at what I think was then called the Junior Turf Club—the coffee stall at Hyde Park Corner. Yes, I certainly learnt how to have fun in London.

All my fancy-dress parties sprang from the time I first saw a charade in the house of Mrs Syrie Wellcome. The volatile and indefatigable Syrie was the daughter of the founder of the wonderful Dr Barnardo's homes and first married Henry— later Sir Henry—Solomon Wellcome, born in a log cabin at Almond, Wisconsin, who established the great firm of manufacturing chemists, Burroughs, Wellcome & Co. Later Syrie married Somerset Maugham. But it was in her house that the charade fixed itself in my mind and I later developed it in ideas for my own parties. The charade demands competition and originality and challenge from a party, and that's what I believe makes for a party's success, the challenge of the imagination and the wits.

Next to Syrie Maugham's house in the King's Road, Chelsea, there lived at Argyll House another woman who also believed in that challenge, Lady Colefax, the wife of an eminent patent lawyer, greatly loved by his friends for his sweetness of character. Of course, you have heard the old quip, 'Nothing was heard in London but the sound of Lady Colefax climbing and climbing.' True or not, she nevertheless had the gift—and I think it is a gift, for it is certainly not to be found in everyone

—of attracting interesting and distinguished people, artists, musicians, writers, American, English, French. I met Bernard Shaw there and Lord Haldane, and it was through meeting Haldane that I later came to know Einstein.

Of course, people were jealous of Lady Colefax, or envious of her or disgruntled because they were not numbered among her guests. There was one famous evening on which she was giving one of her larger and greater parties when that renowned literary trio, the Sitwells, installed a loudspeaker in a car and as the door of Argyll House opened to admit each guest they wittily and pungently mis-announced every name.

On one occasion Sybil Colefax's hospitality did try me to the limits of my endurance. Not by reason of the matter but the manner in which she insisted on our attending her literary *bonne bouche*.

"Elsa," she telephoned me, "I have a treat for you tonight. John Drinkwater is coming and he is going to read his play *Abraham Lincoln* to us—isn't that wonderful?"

I certainly thought so, but was a trifle surprised to find not three or four but fifty invited to listen to the play. Then came further surprise: while the majority of the other guests remained in the large drawing-room with a handsomely laden buffet, eating, drinking, and dancing, a handful of us were ushered into a small white salon by Sybil, who duly presented us to the gaunt figure of John Drinkwater. With me were Lady Oxford and Asquith, Lady Diana Cooper, Sir Edward—'Eddie'—Marsh, the distinguished civil servant, dilettante, and writer, who had for several years been Sir Winston Churchill's private secretary, and a few others. The introductions completed, Sybil withdrew and, as she did so, locked the door *on the outside*. I looked around: I think the only eyebrows that did not rise at that moment must have been John Drinkwater's.

The reading began. It is no criticism of the author or his play to say that he hardly commanded our undivided attention. From the next room came all the sounds of a gay and amusing party. I would not suggest that we turned a deaf ear to John Drinkwater's excellent work, but it was certainly a distracted one. I could see Lady Oxford and Asquith's shoe tapping in time to the dance music that was coming from next door. I gazed through one of the open French windows that led into the garden. Suddenly, a tall, diaphanous figure seemed to float towards that open window, poise a moment, and then jump. I looked around. Diana Cooper was no longer with us. She had taken the one way out from our prison.

On and on went John Drinkwater. Rage mounted within me, I was furious that Diana had escaped and we were still captive. Now another figure was silhouetted against the open window, paused for a second, and disappeared. Eddie Marsh had gone. The author was quite oblivious of his diminishing audience, his eyes were fixed upon his manuscript. I longed to go too, but felt I was too fat for the jump, as there was quite a drop between window and garden. Lady Oxford and Asquith, too, seemed to have misgivings as to following in the others' footsteps. Noisier and noisier grew the sounds from the adjacent party, it was impossible to give one's mind to the play. Finally I seized a moment when Drinkwater paused, either at the end of a scene or an act, and suggested he might appreciate a few minutes' rest. At that moment the key turned in the lock; Sir Arthur Colefax had come to our rescue.

Margot Asquith took a fancy to me, which was extraordinary considering that I was American and she didn't like Americans. It was to me that she made her famous remark, "What a pity when Christopher Columbus discovered America that he ever mentioned it."

One day she tackled me on the subject of my nationality.

"You know, Elsa, it's difficult to believe you're an American. You don't talk like one. Are you sure you weren't born in England?"

"Quite sure," I answered. "And as to the way I talk, well, you don't speak as though you were born in Lancashire or Lord Oxford as though he were a Welshman. I don't know how many counties there are in England, but I'm sure you've just as many accents as we have in America. If I'd been born in the Middle West I'd have said when we were introduced, 'Gosh! Gee! Lady Oxford, it sure is good to meet-ya.' And I suppose you'd never have spoken to me again."

Margot ruled her home and her friends with a rod of iron, though The Wharf, Sutton Courtney, where she and her family spent every weekend, was a fascinating place to visit. It was my first incursion into a world of real literary intelligentsia. I'll never forget my astonishment on coming down to dinner one night to find Lord Oxford and Asquith reading under one lamp, his daughter, Elizabeth Bibesco, reading under another, and his son, Cyril, reading under a third. All three were reading Greek classics in the original version as though they were the most hair-raising thrillers, or the most un-put-downable love stories. Which, I suppose, is what they can be if you know where to look.

I was hardly asked on account of my literary graces, I was asked on account of my bridge. Margot had a passion for the game and was completely absorbed by it, like Maxine Elliott. In fact, guests were only invited if she thought they possessed the equivalent of a PhD at the game. She was not as witty or brittle or as engagingly amusing as Nancy Astor, though woe betide anyone who crossed words with her—they were likely to find the dagger-point of their remarks plunged deeply into their own breast. She had, too, a gift of turning anything to her own advantage, of being blissfully unaware of, or ignoring, hostile remarks.

Her niece, Mrs Clare Beck, who was formerly married to Lord Tennyson, told me of such an occasion when they had gone to a ball at Buckingham Palace. On leaving they were waiting for their car on the steps of the Palace with the crowd gazing in through the railings. Margot, as usual, was dressed in the lowest of low-cut evening gowns, with her cape thrown back revealing her rather attenuated shoulders and smoking a cigarette through almost a foot-long holder. This somewhat unusual apparition naturally caught the attention of the crowd, who began to boo.

Turning to her niece, behind her, she said with great delight, "Just listen to the darlings. You see, they haven't forgotten me since my days at Downing Street."

She was furious with Lord Askwith, the eminent lawyer and arbitrator, when he did not change his name on being raised to the peerage. She made it quite plain to me when he was a fellow guest at The Wharf that he was not a member of the family. Only when we were at the station on our way back to town did her pent-up indignation have the chance to let fly. As the porter was putting the luggage on the train, Lord Askwith said to him, "Don't forget my golf-sticks, porter."

Margot shuddered. "Oh! Askwith," she cried. "Don't say golf-sticks. It's like dropping your aitches in Scotland." I always felt she gave a sigh of relief when the peerage became extinct on his death in 1942.

I remember driving with her to the station one day when we ran into an enormous flock of sheep, that naturally made us fear we might miss the train. Looking down into the baaing sea of foolish faces, she murmured to me, "How strange they called the Saviour the Lamb of God."

Often outrageous in her behaviour, loving the role of enfant terrible, she was, much as I liked her, a dangerous person to invite to a party, for she would do anything to bring the limelight upon her, to hold the centre of the stage. I was giving a small dance for the Duke of Edinburgh's father and mother when they were living in exile in Paris, the Duchess of Kent's mother and father, Prince and Princess Nicolas of Greece, and Prince Christopher and his wife, the former Mrs W. B. Leeds, the American tin-plate heiress. Margot heard of this party and called me up to know if she might come and bring her daughter, Princess Bibesco.

"Of course," I said, "but it's only a dinner and dance."

"Are you suggesting, Elsa, that I'm no longer interested in dancing?" she asked acidly. "Well, I am; I love it."

So I sent them an invitation. As I've said, I always feared her a little because of her unpredictability, that streak of exhibitionism in her character, because there was no knowing to what lengths she would go to attract attention to herself. However, all went well, and after dinner, while everyone was contentedly dancing a fox-trot, I left the ballroom of the Ritz to chat with Prince Christopher of Greece—he later married a sister of the Comte de Paris, Pretender to the throne of France, always the gayest and most gallant of escorts.

While we were talking, I suddenly sensed a momentary silence in the ballroom and then to my surprise the band began to play an old-fashioned waltz. Now I always believe that once a rhythm has been established at a party it must be kept going, mounting steadily and not dropping away. What on earth could the band be doing, disobeying my orders? I hurried back to the ballroom and there, with all my astonished guests looking on in amazement, was Margot doing a *pas seul* in the middle of the empty floor. Gently, but firmly, I led her off and told the band to go on with a livelier tune.

It was typical of her. All eyes had to be on Margot. On

another occasion she asked me to take her to lunch with friends of mine at Versailles, the Prince and Princess Bassiano —he is now the Duke of Sermoneto; a scientist and composer himself, their villa was ever the meeting-place of brilliant intellectuals and artists. But what did Margot do as we entered their drawing-room, where their other guests were assembled to meet her, but pick up her skirts high above those spindly legs and dance a minuet!

She was intensely jealous of others whom she felt in any way encroached on her personal glory. The property adjoining The Wharf, when I knew her, belonged to Mrs Noël Lindsay, a relation of the Duke of Rutland, who was a passionate gardener. I was always told that Nora knew more about flowers than any woman in England. A claim, of course, pooh-poohed by Margot, who implied that she knew more than Nora had ever begun to learn.

Mrs Lindsay's great pride at that moment was a Siberian blue poppy; indeed, she believed she was the first woman in the country to have produced a bloom. After a long night at bridge I went over one Sunday morning while staying at The Wharf in order to see Nora and her famous flower. I found her in tears.

Leading me into the garden, she took me to one of the beds. "Someone has stolen my blue poppy," she said between sobs. "My most precious possession. I took such pride in growing it. Who could possibly want to do a thing like that? After all, it has no value except to me. Who could it have been?" She pointed to the soil near where the poppy had grown. "Look! Do you see that mark? Exactly like a high-heeled shoe. The thief must have been a woman."

I said nothing, though I had my suspicions. Later that morning at lunch I recounted the story of Nora's loss.

Lady Oxford sniffed. "Nora always has these tales of woe," she said. "Quite obviously, it must have been destroyed by some animal."

I fixed Margot with a glittering eye. "It's a very curious animal that wears high-heel shoes," I murmured.

Margot darted a slightly startled look at me. She knew I knew. Despite her faults you could not help liking this fabulous character. Everything she did while I knew her remains as fresh in my mind as if it happened yesterday. Mark

Bonham-Carter, whom I met recently, reminded me strangely of his remarkable grandmother, while, of course, her son, 'Puffin' Asquith, by his brilliant production and direction of so many good British films, has certainly fulfilled his mother's hopes for her youngest offspring. Yes, a remarkable, provoking personality. I know of no one like her today.

Only once did a man actually pack up and move out of his own house to turn it over to me, lock, stock, and barrel, so that I could give perhaps the most spectacular and beautiful party of all. He was Baron Nicholas de Guinsbourg, now on *Vogue* in New York. On June 13th, 1931, I put on a *fête champêtre*, or rural gala, at Nicky's house in the Bois de Boulogne, which was transformed into a glorified farmhouse by the late brilliant artist and scene designer Christian Bérard, who painted a fantastic farmyard on wood frames, and covered the entire house with blue satin. Nicky's face was a study when he arrived with the other 400 guests. Cole Porter had composed a special score for the orchestra to play, and Lauritz Melchior and Frieda Leider sang the love duet from *Tristan und Isolde*. Serge Lifar made a grand entrance naked on a white horse, his body painted entirely in gold. There would be far less unrest abroad in the world if all farmers were as gay as our 400 'peasants'. The Cole Porters arrived in a Sicilian donkey-cart loaded with orchids and gardenias. Linda Porter was the most beautiful woman there. Daisy Fellowes came as Circe with the Baroness Lillian Lo Monaco as her bewitched swine. Bérard's backdrop and the costumes were so beautiful that the event was covered in an entire issue of *L'Illustration*, France's famous art magazine, as though it were covering an exhibition.

Now no one has to tell me that few people have the facilities, much less the money, to entertain so lavishly. Lord knows I wasn't able to do it. In the decade following the First World War I lived in tiny, two-room apartments and the only servant I had was a cleaning woman who came in twice a week. I barely had enough money to meet normal expenses. Yet it was during that period that I made my reputation as a hostess. How? I threw convention out of the window.

You say you haven't adequate space or servants for a proper sit-down dinner? So what? A buffet dinner is much more fun anyway. Guests are free to circulate and mingle with everyone instead of being anchored at a table with their partners on either side of them. Any informal touch tends to break down reserve and make for conviviality in a group. A buffet is cheaper, too. A hostess can get by nicely with one main course, salad and dessert. The food must be simple, of necessity, since guests serve themselves and eat under makeshift conditions. There is another advantage in a buffet that solves a ticklish problem for the hostess who does not have complete sets of china, glasses, and silverware. In the pleasant milling around, critical guests are less apt to notice that the table appointments do not match perfectly. It's a triviality, perhaps, but it disturbs the oversensitive hostess.

What about the preparation of the dinner? That headache can be turned into the highlight of the evening by adopting a suggestion which, at first shock, appears to be a brainstorm. Have the men cook the dinner. Men always brag that cooking is a cinch they can master any time they put their hands to it. Call their bluff by turning them loose on an easy recipe that can be salvaged no matter how badly it is manhandled— something like spaghetti and meat sauce, shrimps creole, or Welsh rarebit. I won't vouch for results, but I can promise a hilarious hour while the men are making messes of themselves and the kitchen.

No one will mind that dinner is late. Half the guests will declare, to a man, that they never had a better dinner. If wives are as smart as I know they are, they will play along with the gag on the off-chance that their husbands will get delusions of grandeur and relieve them occasionally of kitchen duty. That's beside the point. Even if the dinner is a culinary catastrophe, it will be fun at the moment, and that's the main purpose in giving a party.

Food doesn't make or break a party. A chef with the *Cordon Bleu* can prepare dinner and the evening still can fall as flat as a cold soufflé. The critical turning point of a party comes after dinner. That's when the ordinary hostess sees her party slough off into one of two ruts. Guests sit around and make desultory conversation or they play cards. In either case, it is a dull, static routine and the hostess pays heavily for it in the liquor lapped up. Most people drink to escape boredom. They don't need bottled stimulation if they are shown how to draw upon their own resources for amusement.

The consumption of liquor at my parties always was astonishingly low—and I had more than my share of cut-ups who were waging crusades to keep the distilleries of France and England working overtime. Excessive drinking turned only one of my parties into a rowdy affair. That was the Come As You Were party I gave in Paris in 1927. The big idea was that the sixty guests were pledged to appear dressed exactly as they were when the invitations were received. To make sure of a wide variety of get-ups, I had the invitations delivered by messengers at odd hours of the day and night.

Knowing my customers as well as I did, I chartered two buses and personally picked them up at their homes. Parisians are accustomed to strange sights but, after all, there are limits to their tolerance. Hiring the private buses proved to be a necessary precaution. The Marquis de Polignac was attired in full evening dress save for one conspicuous omission. He wasn't wearing his trousers. Daisy Fellowes carried her lace panties in her hand. A half dozen women who are respectable grandmothers today came in slips that definitely were not shadow-proof. Bebe Bérard wore a dressing-gown, a telephone attached to his ear, and had white makeup on his face to simulate shaving cream. Several men who rated honour above vanity came in hair-nets. Jay O'Brien was a fashionplate in tails except for one minor detail. He wasn't wearing a white tie, and somehow he looked more disreputable than anyone.

I made two mistakes in my otherwise careful planning. I installed a bar in each bus and I neglected to account for Paris's monumental traffic jams in my time-table. The buses began to pick up people at seven o'clock in the evening, but it was nine o'clock before they arrived at Meraud Guevara's apartment in Montparnasse, which I had borrowed for the occasion. By that time everyone was flying so high that there were drastic changes in some of the costumes. Countess Gabriella Robilant, an Italian, lost her skirt during manœuvres in one of the landgoing hangars. Gabriella was unconcerned, but Countess Elisabeth de Bretueil, a Frenchwoman, was outraged.

"I refuse to be seen in my own country with anyone in that scandalous condition," she said indignantly.

"To the Bastille!" Gabriella cried, yanking off Elisabeth's skirt. "Now a French and an Italian countess are equals."

I gave up trying to bring the situation under control after a plea for a little restraint was answered by a volley of hard rolls fired at me by my guests. The neighbours cheered my hasty retreat. They didn't want spoil-sports, including the police, throwing a wet blanket over the free floor show in the garden. It looked like the rehearsal of a French bedroom farce.

There are safer gambits for getting guests to throw off their inhibitions at a party. My favourite device for giving a dull gathering a shot in the arm is a game, the sillier the better. I know it sounds corny, but it never failed to work for me with people who make a fetish of sophistication or fancy themselves too dignified to lend themselves to that sort of thing. Personally, I prefer guessing games that test wit and knowledge—Twenty Questions, Categories, charades, and the like —but they backfire if all the participants are not on the same general intellectual level. In a large group a few players usually wind up dominating the game, and those who are not as quick on the uptake retire to the sidelines with a feeling of inferiority. The best games are those in which failure is comical rather than embarrassing.

The list of possibilities is almost endless. For example, to demonstrate how the sense of smell is governed by visual association, have blindfolded players identify a series of familiar articles without touching them. The ludicrous answers will give everyone a laugh. Bananas will be tagged as violets and a sprig of parsley as expensive perfume. A hostess can save enough on liquor bills to buy herself a new hat by putting up an eighty-nine-cent bottle of domestic wine as the prize in an absurd contest such as button-sewing or draping a live model with a few yards of cheap material for the most stylish effect. The Mayfair set once rooted more frantically for their entries in a race I put on than it ever did at Epsom Downs. The entries were mechanical wind-up toys I borrowed from friends with children.

What if you're stuck with stuffed shirts who refuse to play along with your amiable stunts? I'm tempted to suggest that you cross them off your list, but I realize it may be necessary to entertain them for business or social reasons. Every hostess I know tries to make the best of a sticky situation by balancing bores with bright, amusing people at the same party. It never works. One group cramps the style of the other and, as always, mediocrity pulls talent down to its level. Attack the problem boldly. Fight fire with fire. If you *must* have bores, always put them together or at the same table, and be prepared for a surprise that must be seen to be believed.

For some reason I've never been able to understand, bores have an effervescent chemical reaction on one another at a party. They invariably have a marvellous time trading banalities in the absence of competition. Clichés roll trippingly off the tongue like sparkling epigrams and trite observations acquire depth sinking into receptive minds. Don't ask me why. I only know it is an unfailing phenomenon. It's worth a try accepting my word for it. Anything is better, as far as I'm concerned, than the alternative catch-all for repaying second-class social debts—a cocktail party.

The cocktail party is easily the worst invention since castor oil. I've never given a cocktail party and I'd sooner go to the dentist than be found at one of those social abominations. The disorganized routs always are flops because they violate the first principle of party-giving. The host and hostess must have a good time themselves if their guests are to spend a few pleasant hours in their home. That is manifestly impossible under the conditions that attend a typical mob scene.

You know what usually happens. The condemned couple greet you at the door with a clammy hand and a despairing eye. They know better than anyone the torture about to be inflicted on you. They can't accommodate all the people who have been invited and each new arrival means so many more decibels of noise and so many more gallons of noxious cigarette smoke. Everyone is screaming and smoking in self-defence. The limp anchovies on soggy biscuits are an offence to your stomach and it is compounded by lukewarm, prefabricated drinks. The hostess anxiously wonders how many diehards will hang on to the bitter end in the delusion that dinner will be served. The host wonders how long his liquor and ice will hold out and decides to make deep inroads into both in the hope that everyone will go home when nothing is left to drink. Eventually, and not a moment too soon, the condemned couple are reprieved by the fatigue that drives their guests into the night in search of a place to sit down.

Inadequate seating arrangements may seem to be a minor

detail, but it has ruined more parties than any other single factor. I didn't go to Perle Mesta's ball the night of Queen Elizabeth's Coronation, but friends who were there told me it was a fiasco. The ball was held in a long, narrow room at Londonderry House and there wasn't a comfortable chair in the place where a guest could escape being trampled by the aimless, milling crowd. The small fortune Mrs Mesta spent on the ball went down the drain. The notables left early. No one can be impressed when they find no chairs to sit on or that the right people are all at Buckingham Palace. A lesson to be learned: never give a rival party when the opposition has all the tricks.

More than one woman since Lot's wife has betrayed herself by looking back, but I can't help shedding a nostalgic tear for the decline of my favourite entertainment—the costume party. I've given so many dress-up soirées that Janet Flanner once described my party activities under the generic title of Come as Somebody Else. I suppose the ham in me partly accounts for my fondness for costume balls. I always had the uncanny knack, even when I was much younger, of getting tricked up to look like any elder statesman I chose to impersonate. Among my rôles were Herbert Hoover, Ben Franklin, Edouard Herriot, and Aristide Briand. On one occasion my makeup fooled entirely too many people.

During the Peace Conference in 1919, Prince Murat picked me up in his car on the way to a costume ball in Paris. The Prince was masquerading as Clemenceau and I as Lloyd George, the respective leaders of the French and English delegations to the Conference. Passers-by caught a glimpse of us as we rode down the Champs-Elysées and thought we were the diplomats in the flesh. In three minutes traffic was blocked by the dense, cheering crowd that surrounded the car. I explained to the frantic gendarme trying to clear the jam that we were impersonating the heroes.

"You *are* Lloyd George and Clemenceau," he whispered furiously. "Bow to the crowd and tip your hats. There will be a riot if it is discovered that you are imposters. I will do nothing to protect you from the physical violence you deserve."

I remember at this party being particularly struck by an attractive, sleek, rather slinky young woman in a kilt. She turned out to be half American and half European, a mixture that, like the whisky of the New World and the vermouth of the Old, can produce a subtle blend. She was the Hon. Mrs Reginald Fellowes, and for her fashion and her fascination she was to become as much a legend as had her grandfather, on her mother's side, Isaac Merritt Singer, for his invention of the sewing machine.

A daughter of the fourth Duc Decazes, she had been married very early to Prince Jean de Broglio, by whom she had a very beautiful daughter, Emmeline, now the Comtesse de Casteja. When I came to know her she had already been widowed and was the wife of Lord De Ramsey's son. Daisy Fellowes was often hailed by the fashion writers as the best-dressed woman in the world, but it was by no conventional means she earned this distinction. Money was not the sole secret of her wardrobe; she could have afforded the most expensive, but more often she relied on instinctive flair.

She knew all the tricks of her sex and played them off on other women to her own advantage. She refused to follow the crowd, she had always to strike out on a line of her own. While it was the fashion for everyone to go to Molyneux or Patou or Chanel, Daisy would forage off the byways of the boulevards to discover some dressmaker who could carry out her ideas. It was like that she brought fame and fortune to Louise Boulanger. For if Daisy did not follow others, others were quite happy to follow Daisy. Invited to some elaborate party where she knew everyone would be gorgeously attired, Daisy would have recourse to one of her dressmakers, buy a simple black dress as worn by a midinette, alter it in some way, add some original accessory—and have all the women green with envy for creating a new fashion, which, of course, they quickly copied.

I remember them tearing their hair when she borrowed the idea of wearing something like a man's dinner-jacket covered in sequins. There was the night, too, when I gave a *diner des bijoux*. Everyone had to pile on every jewel they could lay hands on. And, naturally, they all arrived looking like something out of the Arabian Nights. But not Daisy. All she wore was a perfectly plain black dress, but with a belt of diamonds round her waist almost a foot deep! She certainly had the art of being provokingly unpredictable on every occasion.

Into the Daisy chain of her wide circle of friends there

drifted at this time an amusing fellow, Hugo Rumbold, brother of the former Ambassador to Germany, Sir Horace Rumbold. Now Hugo was a great mimic with an unappeasable appetite for dressing up as somebody else. Even though people knew he was going to do it, knew he was going to be present, they could not recognize him. He once fooled an entire house-party while staying with Lord Latham and pretending to be his maiden aunt. He stuttered badly, but when singing, reciting, or pretending to be someone else it disappeared. The horrors we once suffered one night at a party when he rose to recite 'The Czar is no more, he lies in his gore . . .' and suddenly realized that the Grand Duchess Marie, cousin of the Czar, was present!

I'll never forget the night when Daisy invited an imposing array of guests to meet the new Portuguese Ambassador to Paris, the Marquis di San Pedro Porto—or some such name. No one saw through his French and English laced with a heavy Portuguese accent, or suspected him in any way, till he took off his moustache and we found it was Hugo after all.

Another time Daisy and myself and Dickie Gordon were invited by Lady Diana Cooper and her husband to dine with them, and Daisy asked if she might bring a Spanish woman who, she said, was a very well-known but rather eccentric authoress. The woman, however, turned out to be the success of the party. Duff Cooper was quite taken by her charm and witty conversation, so much so that when we went on to a night club he was the first to ask her to dance. But I noticed that hardly had he placed his arm about her and embarked on the steps of a tango than he quickly led her back to the table and sat as far away from her as possible.

"What's the matter, Duff?" Dickie Gordon asked.

"I don't know," Duff replied. Then he whispered to Daisy, "I don't think I like that friend of yours as much as I thought."

At which Daisy and Dickie burst out laughing. It was Hugo Rumbold again. Dickie had spent all day fitting him into her clothes, taking him to the hairdresser to arrange his wig, even lacing him into his corsets before the party.

Once Daisy and I gave a ball in her house in the Rue St James, at Neuilly. Again it was fancy dress, everybody being asked to come as some famous personality. After my success as Lloyd George, I thought I would go as another Prime

Minister, Monsieur Briand, because it gave me the chance of wearing a bushy soup-strainer moustache, which I always think adds such distinction to my looks. The Baroness Lo Monaco, who always loved to dress up, went as the Aga Khan, and Daisy's aunt, Princess Edmond de Polignac by marriage, and a Singer heiress by birth, as a famous French author. All went well until people began asking me "Where's Daisy?"

I couldn't tell them, for I didn't know. I hadn't seen or recognized her and I presumed she just hadn't turned up for her own party. I could only think she had decided at the last moment to do something else. It would be quite like her. The only thing that puzzled me was the presence of that almost national French character outside the ladies' cloakroom, a *dame des lavabos*. Hardly usual in a private house, of course, but I could only imagine that Daisy had obtained her services for the evening to help the servants. Anyway, there she sat in sepulchral black and with the inevitable shawl over her head, knitting away in front of a table or assisting the ladies as they entered and emerged, appropriately armed with a serviette in her hand and on the table a conspicuously placed plate to receive *pourboires*. I must say it shook all of us to the core when somebody in the small hours of the morning unmasked that dame des lavabos as no less than Daisy herself.

There is a sound psychological basis for the fact that every costume party in my experience has been a rousing success. By identifying themselves with another character or historical period people assume new personalities and the change usually is a distinct improvement. There is a touch of the Walter Mitty in all of us. We love to romanticize ourselves and imagine we are fascinating and/or dashing creatures, and a costume party is an ideal springboard for fanciful flights. I'm told that costume parties, once popular on all social levels, have been supplanted by movies, television, soap operas, and other synthetic escapes from drab reality. That's only half the story.

I know the course of history will not be altered an iota if no one ever gets tricked out again as Marie Antoinette or Don Juan. To me, though, the whole thing is symptomatic of an attitude with broader implications. People simply are too lazy to take the trouble of expressing their individuality even in an area as inconsequential as a party. It is said that costume affairs are expensive. Ridiculous. It is cheaper to hire a costume than it is to go out and buy a new dress—and what's the matter with a home-made outfit that shows a spark of ingenuity?

Actually, a costume affair is the easiest party to run. You merely select a theme and the guests will take it from there, making their own fun. What theme? There are dozens of motifs that can be developed without renting eighteenth-century gowns and silk knee-breeches. According to the 1950 census, only 0·0008 per cent of the population in the United States is of full-blooded Indian stock. All the rest of us are descended from immigrants. Have guests come in costumes that denote the foreign origins of their families. For an amusing switch, guests can satirize national traits with gag props ranging from a piggy bank for the Scots to a stolen toy horse for countries that shall be nameless here. A party pegged to outmoded fashions in clothes always is a howl. (Remember the shapeless flour-sacks of the 1920s and the Princess Eugenie hats of the 1930s?) The outfits can be found in closets and attics people have been meaning to clean out for years. One of the most hilarious—and revealing—affairs I ever gave was a Come As Your Opposite party. Had it been cricket to do so, I could have met my expenses selling tickets to psychiatrists.

I hope I've demonstrated that the knack of giving good parties involves no special talent or training. It requires only a desire to improvise fresh ideas and the willingness to spend a little time developing them. My one regret is that I lavished too much time on parties, an effort that could have been devoted to more aesthetic pursuits. I wish I had written a sonnet that is reprinted in an obscure anthology or composed an enduring song that is whistled in the still of the night. Yet there is a certain satisfaction in being the best in any field, even if it is as superficial as painting Easter eggs, hitting a golf ball into a tin cup, or giving parties. After all, not every hostess has had the distinction of being denounced twice in the House of Commons as a menace to the dignity of the British Empire.

The reprimands were aftermaths of two frolics that were projects rather than parties, considering the planning that went into them. The first one was my famous—or should it be infamous?—scavenger hunt in Paris in 1927. A gallon jar of Patou's Joy perfume was offered as a prize to the player who brought back in one hour the most items, or the most unusual specimen, on a list. The objectives were a slipper taken from Mistinguett on the stage of the Casino de Paris; a black swan from the lake in the Bois de Boulogne; a *pot de chambre*; three hairs plucked from a red-headed woman (the Duchesse of D'yen, a flaming red-head, locked herself in a room to protect herself); a pompom off the cap of a French sailor; a work animal; and a handkerchief from the Baron Maurice de Rothschild's house.

The players took off, and a series of disturbances promptly broke out all over Paris. The manager of the Casino de Paris put in a riot call for the police when two hoodlums barged on the stage and grabbed Mistinguett's slippers, then ransacked the shoes in her dressing-room, forcing her to finish the performance in bare feet. The black swan in the Bois, a vile-tempered beast, put up such a fight that two bird fanciers went to the hospital for repairs. My landlady had hysterics when a donkey, borrowed from a pedlar, started to kick out the walls of my apartment. The Grand Duchess Marie of Russia played a lone hand and came back with the trophy that won first prize. It was a most unaristocratic exhibit—a pot de chambre with two big, blue inquisitive eyes painted on the inside.

The following day a man from the Sûreté Nationale paid me a visit that was not entirely unexpected. He accused me of instigating heinous crimes, ranging from the riot at the Casino to attempted robbery of public property in the Bois. He went away, quietly and quickly, when I informed him that the rowdies who had insulted Mistinguett were Robert de Castellane, the Mayor of Paris's son, and the nephew of the Prefect of Police.

A more serious *contretemps* was not resolved so easily. It seemed that Lady Elsie de Wolfe Mendl, who was married to Sir Charles, a staff member of the British Embassy in Paris, had created an international incident in going after a French sailor's pompom. She was charged with violating France's sovereignty by invading the Ministere de la Marine and stealing the cap of the sailor on guard duty. A stiff note of protest was despatched to His Majesty's Government, causing a frightful tizzy in the Commons. I was roundly condemned as the pernicious influence responsible for the deplorable action by the wife of one of His Majesty's civil servants in Paris.

Two months later, when the coast was clear, I went to London to stage a murder party at the opening of Lady Ribblesdale's house in St James's Park. Neysa McNein, the American artist, invented the murder game which I had introduced in Europe the previous year at a party given by Lady Mendl in Paris. I became the foremost expert at the game because nobody else was willing to make the elaborate plans necessary to fake a murder that was realistic enough to fool a large group. Ava Ribblesdale, the former Mrs John Jacob Astor, one of the most divinely beautiful women I have ever known—who for some strange reason became a great friend of mine—was witty and mischievous enough to let me arrange this disastrous affair.

Only four people were in on the plot in London—Lady Ribblesdale, her butler, the 'victim', and me. The victim was Zita Youngman, a beautiful girl. The austere Duke of Marlborough was selected as the suspect because he was to be the top-ranking guest at the party and pointing the finger at him would create the greatest excitement. Two weeks before the party I began planting cryptic personal messages in London newspapers as clues which could be construed, at the denouncement, as circumstantial evidence of murky goings-on between Zita and 'M', her distraught admirer.

On the night of the party the company assembled for dinner, but Zita's place at the table was vacant. Lady Ribblesdale casually remarked that Zita must have been detained in her room upstairs and told the butler to serve dinner without her. I was seated next to the Duke, and during dinner I asked him for a cigarette. He handed me a silver case we knew he always carried and I surreptitiously slipped into it two Turkish cigarettes of a brand none of the other guests smoked. The stage was now set to spring the murder.

Lady Ribblesdale, feigning anxiety over Zita's continued absence, told the butler to go to her room to find out whether anything was wrong. The butler came back and said the door was locked and repeated knocking had brought no response. That alarmed everyone and we went upstairs to investigate. Lady Ribblesdale ordered the butler to break down the door. The guests were frozen with horror at the sight in the room.

Zita was lying on the bed with a huge blob of catsup on her breast. A revolver was on the floor.

The butler barred the doorway and ordered everyone to leave, to preserve all possible clues. I pretended to call the police headquarters, and two actors who had been hired to impersonate detectives promptly arrived. They made a quick search of the murder scene and snorted loudly and significantly when they saw the Turkish cigarette that had been planted in an ashtray at the side of the bed.

The detectives told the guests to take their places at the table and requested them to submit their cigarettes for inspection. Several exhibits were examined and cleared before the Duke of Marlborough's turn came. The detectives opened his silver case, then nodded solemnly at each other.

"This confirms our suspicions," a detective said, revealing the Turkish cigarettes I put in the Duke's case. "Can you explain these, Your Grace?"

Marlborough was too thunderstruck to answer.

"Come now, we know all about it," the detective continued. "You had a liaison with the deceased. We've been watching you ever since these threatening messages first appeared." He brandished the cuttings I had put in the papers. In the confusion, no one commented that it was a remarkable coincidence the detective had the cuttings handy. They were passed briefly among the guests to substantiate the charge. The stunned Duke was the picture of black guilt.

"Your Grace," the detective rasped, "why did you murder Zita Youngman?"

That was the cue for the butler to plunge the room into total darkness. He knocked over a chair, stamped on the floor, and slammed the door to produce the sound effects of a fleeing man. Lady Ribblesdale and I screamed. The detectives yelled hoarsely, "Stop that man!" Dishes crashed to the floor. The guests thrashed about in a wild turmoil for thirty seconds, and then the lights went on suddenly. Zita was sitting at the table nibbling on an olive.

The Duke maintained his reputation as a sportsman by smiling feebly at the hoax, but there was the devil to pay when the newspapers got wind of the affair. The *Daily Express* carried the story on page one under an eight-column headline:

DUKE OF MARLBOROUGH MURDERS BEAUTIFUL
GIRL IN LADY RIBBLESDALE'S HOUSE

In smaller type, the subheading read:

Elsa Maxwell Stages a Party

Again, I believe, I was denounced in the Commons for shocking disrespect for one of the noblest peers of the realm. But I was already on my way to Rome to play the murder game with Princess Jane di San Faustino, who was delighted by the rumpus Lady Ribblesdale's party had provoked.

Princess Jane and I selected guests who had not heard of the game, but we neglected to consider that the police of Rome were among the uninitiated. The clues I placed in the papers were so ominous that two honest-to-George detectives wanted to arrest me as a dangerous character.

As I have said, a good party takes a lot of careful planning. I had the foresight to invite Henry Fletcher, our divine American Ambassador to Italy, to the party. When I told Henry what I was up to, he promptly took the police off my neck. Henry, a gallant gentleman of the old school, didn't want a crimp put in his fun.

There was a serious side to the parties I gave in the 1920s— the business of paying for them. Paris was my headquarters, and although the artistic climate was heady and invigorating, I couldn't live on air alone. I needed money for such luxuries as food and rent, especially when Dickie Gordon was in England or batting around the continent with her own group of friends. On such occasions I lived in a series of dismal rabbit-warrens that had two things in common. The rents were cheap and the rooms were on the top floors of old walk-up pensions built in the days when a roof and four walls were regarded as the height of creature comforts. Like Lewis Carroll's Father William, who strengthened his jaws arguing law cases with his wife, the energy I developed climbing stairs in Paris has lasted the rest of my life.

To turn a fast and reasonably honest franc, I became one of Europe's pioneer Press agents. Long before exporting technical aid was a feature of American foreign policy, I was running a private Point Four programme for two of Europe's major industries—its fashions and touring resorts. Today the business of separating visitors from their money is a big business. All countries in Western Europe now maintain government bureaus operating under fancy synonyms for Press agents. The titles are new, but they're using the ideas I was when I was in Paris, Venice, and Monte Carlo.

Art Buchwald

As a riposte—perhaps even as a reprisal—comes another attitude to an Elsa Maxwell party. The column of Art Buchwald in the *New York Herald-Tribune* Paris edition has, for a number of years, specialized in a laconic form of debunking. Buchwald, always a lively and amusing journalist and reporter of Parisian goings-on, is at his best on subjects such as Grace Kelly's first meeting with His Serene Highness. Elsa wasn't invited to the Monte Carlo wedding. This piece of malice from *Art Buchwald's Paris* may suggest the reason. Or maybe Elsa gets the last laugh, after all. Who'd like to bet on it?

⋄

THE PARTY WATCHERS

I was party-watching at Elsa Maxwell's costume ball. A party-watcher differs from a party-goer in that a party-watcher has no desire to go to a party but gets a tremendous kick out of standing on the sidewalk commenting on the people who go to the party.

Dressing to party-watch differs from dressing to party-go because a party-watcher, if too well dressed, will arouse the antagonism of other party-watchers. At the same time, he cannot look too poorly dressed or he will be arrested by the police for being an agitator.

I hit it off just right by wearing a dark brown suit, dark shoes, and a soiled white shirt.

I arrived early at the Laurent Restaurant so I would be assured of a good place. If you come late, chauffeurs and amateur party-watchers (people who are walking their dogs, etc) will have taken the best places.

I got there at eleven, and almost all the good places were taken, but I managed to squeeze in between an American woman of about fifty and a thin Hungarian gentleman who seemed to know everyone that arrived.

While I stood there waiting for the guests, the American woman got into an argument with her husband.

"You go home if you want to. I'm going to stay," she said.

"But what sense is there gawking at a bunch of made-up extras?"

"I enjoy it."

"Well, good night!" And he pushed his way through the crowd and went home.

The American woman turned to me. "My poor husband. I'm a watcher and he isn't."

The guests started to arrive, and all our attention was centred on the Rolls-Royces, Bentleys, Jaguars, and Cadillacs. As each person got out of his car, the murmur went through the crowd: "Who is it? Who is it?"

The guests were identified as they sauntered into the restaurant. The police pushed us back a little so the party-goers wouldn't get too close to the party-watchers. I thought this only fair.

The American woman next to me was full of information.

"You know I was on the same boat as Elsa."

I looked impressed.

"Yes, the Donahues were on the boat, also. Of course, they didn't speak to me, but I saw them every day."

"Every day," I whistled.

"Yes, every day."

The Hungarian man next to me also spoke to me. "You see that woman getting out of the Rolls-Royce. She had a parlay."

"A parlay?"

"Yup. She invited the Duke and Duchess of Windsor to her last three parties and they never came to any of them."

"Look," said the American woman. "There's Orson Welles. I was just sure he would be here tonight. Hello, Orson."

There was no reply.

A little English lady standing next to the American woman spoke up. "You know the theme of this party is to come as somebody you either love or hate the most. Have you noticed 75 per cent of the people have come as themselves?"

The police pushed us back a little farther.

The Hungarian spoke again. "They look as if they're very

annoyed with us standing here, but they'd feel terrible if none of us showed up to look at them."

"How true," I replied.

"Elsa must be champing at the bit," the little English-woman said. "Mrs William Breed didn't come to the party."

"Who's Mrs Breed?" I asked.

The Hungarian man looked disgusted. "Don't you read the Social Register?"

My feet were getting tired so I moved on to the lawn to peek through an open window.

"Get off the lawn," the policeman said.

I got off the lawn and went back to the entrance.

Most of the guests had gone in and the watchers started thinning out. (Party-watchers very rarely stay to the end of the party.)

My American friend was telling a small group about a scandalous affair aboard the ship she came over on, and named several prominent people as participants. I was shocked, and said I didn't believe it.

The American woman said it was true because she was on the ship.

Arturo Lopez arrived in a sleek silver car and called the photographers over to take his picture. They came over and he posed for them in a pink shirt.

The Hungarian man said: "Arturo Lopez. He's worth millions. He doesn't know what to do with his money."

By this time there were only a few of us left. The American woman went home, the Hungarian man disappeared, and almost all the chauffeurs were asleep in their cars.

I thought I'd have one last look into the party and went back to the open window and looked in.

"Get off the grass," the policeman screamed.

I got off the grass and decided to go home and look up Mrs Breed in the Social Register.

Ann Warren Griffith

THE ADVENT of commercial television in Britain has brought with it a new invasion of the home, and a new idiom on the tongue. This satire of Miss Griffith takes the diabolical thing a stage further. She envisages a ventriloquial device which makes the products sing their own praises. Only Grandmother, a superb relic from the past, resists this march of progress. But—as the magazine synopses say—read on. This is a brilliant and salutary tale. I know little of the career of Miss Griffith. For all I know she may be the daughter of D. W. Griffith. She can certainly plan a horrible future for us on the grand scale, and now that the Singing Jingle is already on our children's lips, I'm not sure that what follows is funny at all.

❖

CAPTIVE AUDIENCE

Mavis Bascom read the letter hastily and passed it across the breakfast table to her husband, Fred, who read the first paragraph and exclaimed, "She'll be here this afternoon!" but neither Mavis nor the two children heard him because the cereal box was going 'Boom! Boom!' so loudly. Presently it stopped and the bread said urgently, "One good slice deserves another! How about another slice all round, eh, Mother?" Mavis put four slices into the toaster, and then there was a brief silence. Fred wanted to discuss the impending visit, but his daughter Kitty got in ahead of him, saying:

"Mom, it's my turn to choose the next cereal, and this shot-from-a-cannon stuff is almost gone. Will you take me to the store this afternoon?"

"Yes, dear, of course. I must admit I'll be glad when this box is gone. 'Boom, boom, boom,' that's all it ever says. And some of the others have such nice songs and jingles. I don't see whyever you picked it, Billy."

Billy was about to answer when his father's cigarette package interrupted, "Yessir, time to light up a Chesterfield! Time to enjoy that first mild, satisfying smoke of the day."

Fred lit a cigarette and said angrily, "Mavis, you know I don't like you to say such things in front of the children. It's a perfectly good commercial, and when you cast reflections on one, you're undermining all of them. I won't have you confusing these kids!"

"I'm sorry, Fred," was all Mavis had time to answer, because the salt box began a long and technically very interesting talk on iodization.

Since Fred had to leave for the office before the talk was over, he telephoned back to Mavis about her grandmother's visit. "Mavis," he said, "she can't stay with us! You'll have to get her out just as soon as possible."

"All right, Fred. I don't think she'll stay very long anyway. You know she doesn't like visiting us any more than you like having her."

"Well, the quicker she goes the better. If anybody down here finds out about her I'll be washed up with MV the same day!"

"Yes, Fred, I know. I'll do the best I can."

Fred had been with the Master Ventriloquism Corporation of America for fifteen years. His work had been exceptional in every respect and, unless word leaked out about Mavis's grandmother, he could expect to remain with it for the rest of his life. He had enjoyed every step of the way from office-boy to his present position as Assistant Vice-President in Charge of Sales, though he sometimes wished he could have gone into the technical end of it. Fascinating, those huge batteries of machines pouring out their messages to the American people. It seemed to him almost miraculous, the way the commercials were broadcast into thin air and picked up by the tiny discs embedded in the bottle or can or box or whatever wrapping contained the product, but he knew it involved some sort of electronic process that he couldn't understand. Such an incredibly complex process, yet unfailingly accurate! He had never heard of the machines making a mistake; never, for instance, had they thrown a shoe-polish commercial so that it came out of a hair-tonic bottle. Intrigued though he was by the mechanical intricacies of Master Ventriloquism, however, he had no head for that sort of thing, and was content to make his contribution in the sales end.

And quite a contribution it was. Already in the two short years since his promotion to Assistant Vice-President he had signed up two of the toughest clients that had ever been brought into the MV camp. First had been the telephone company, now one of the fattest accounts on the Corporation's books. They had held out against MV for years, until he, Fred, hit upon the idea that sold them—a simple message to come from every telephone, at fifteen-minute intervals throughout the MV broadcasting day, reminding people to look in the directory before dialling information. After the telephone company coup, Fred became known around the Corporation as a man to watch. He hadn't rested on his laurels. He had, if anything, topped his telephone performance. MV had pretty much given up hope of selling its services to the dignified, the conservative New York *Times*. But Fred went ahead and did it. He'd kept the details a secret from Mavis. She'd see it for the first time tomorrow morning. Tomorrow morning! Damn! Grandmother would be here. You could bet she'd make some crack and spoil the whole thing.

Fred honestly didn't know if he would have gone ahead and married Mavis if he'd known about her grandmother.

For the sad fact of the matter was that Grandmother had never adjusted to MV. She was the only person he and Mavis knew who still longed for the 'good old days', as she called them, the days before MV, and she yapped about them ad nauseam. She and her 'A man's home is his castle'—if he'd heard her say it once he'd heard her say it 500 times. Unfortunately, it wasn't just that Grandmother was a boring old fool who refused to keep up with the times. The sadder fact of the matter was that she had broken the law, and today was finishing a five-year prison term. Did any other man here at MV have such a cross to bear?

Again and again he and Mavis had warned Grandmother that her advanced years would not keep her from being clapped into jail, and they hadn't. She'd gone absolutely wild on the day the Supreme Court had handed down the Earplug Decision. It was the climax of a long and terribly costly fight by the MV Corporation. The sale of earplugs had grown rapidly during the years MV was expanding, and just at a peak period, when MV had over 3000 accounts, National Earplug Associates, Inc., had boldly staged a country-wide campaign advertising earplugs as the last defence against MV. The success of the campaign was such that the Master Ventriloquism Corporation found itself losing hundreds of accounts. MV sued immediately and the case dragged through the courts for years. Judges had a hard time making up their minds. Some sections of the Press twaddled about 'captive audiences'. The MV Corporation felt reasonably certain that the Supreme Court justices were sensible men, but with its very existence at stake there was nerve-racking suspense until the decision was made. National Earplug Associates, Inc., was found guilty of Restraint of Advertising, and earplugs were declared unconstitutional.

Grandmother, who was visiting Fred and Mavis at the time, hit the ceiling. She exhausted herself and them with her tirades, and swore that never never never would she give up her earplugs.

MV's representatives in Washington soon were able to get Congress to put teeth into the Supreme Court's decision, and eventually, just as Fred and Mavis predicted, Grandmother joined the ridiculous band who went to jail for violating the law prohibiting the use or possession of earplugs.

That was some skeleton for anybody, let alone an executive of MV, to have in his closet! Luckily, it had, up to now, remained in the closet, for at no time during her trial or afterwards did Grandmother mention having a relative who worked for the Corporation. But they had been lulled into a false sense of security. They assumed that Grandmother would die before finishing her prison term and that the problem of Grandmother was, therefore, solved. Now they were faced with it all over again. How were they going to keep her from shooting off her mouth before their friends and neighbours? How persuade her to go away and live in some distant spot?

Fred's secretary broke in on these worrisome thoughts, bringing him an unusually large batch of morning mail. "Seems there's kind of an unfavourable reaction to the new Pratt's Airotsac campaign. Forty-seven letters of protest already—read 'em and weep," she said saucily, and returned to her own office.

Fred picked a letter out of the pile and read:

Dear Sirs,

Like most mothers, I give my baby Pratt's Airotsac every time she cries for it. For the past few days, however, it has seemed to me that she has cried for it much more often than usual. Then I heard about the new Pratt's Airotsac commercial, and caught on that part of the time it wasn't my baby but the MV baby crying. I think it's a very cute idea, but am wondering if you could possibly use another baby because the one you have now sounds so much like mine and I cannot tell them apart so I do not know when my baby is actually crying for Pratt's Airotsac and when it's the MV baby.

Thanking you in advance for anything you can do about this, and with all good wishes for your continued success, I am,

MRS. MONA P. HAYES

Fred groaned and flipped through some of the other letters. The story was the same—mothers not knowing whether it was their own baby or the MV baby and consequently confused as to when to administer the medicine. Dopes! Why didn't they have sense enough to put the Airotsac bottle at the other end of the house from the baby, and then they could tell by the direction the sound came from whether it was a bona-fide baby or an advertising baby! Well, he'd have to figure out some way to change it, since many of the letters reported babies getting sick from overdoses. The Master Ventriloquism Corporation certainly didn't want to be responsible for that sort of thing.

Underneath the forty-seven complaints was a memo from the Vice-President in Charge of Sales, congratulating Fred on his brilliant handling of the New York *Times*. Ordinarily, this would have made it a red-letter day, but what with Grandmother and Pratt's, Fred's day was already ruined.

Mavis's day was not going well either.

She felt uneasy, out-of-sorts, and in the lull between the Breakfast Commercials and the Cleaning Commercials she tried to analyse her feelings. It must be Grandmother. Perhaps it was true, as Fred said, that Grandmother was a bad influence. It wasn't that she was *right*. Mavis believed in Fred, because he was her husband, and believed in the MV Corporation, because it was the largest corporation in the entire United States. Nevertheless, it upset her when Fred and Grandmother argued, as they almost always did when they were together.

Anyway, maybe this time Grandmother wouldn't be so troublesome. Maybe jail had taught her how wrong it was to try to stand in the way of progress. On this hopeful note her thinking ended for the soap powder box cried out, "Good morning, Mother! What say we go after those breakfast dishes and give our hands a beauty treatment at the same time? You know, Mother, no other soap gives you a beauty treatment *while* you wash your dishes. Only So-Glow, So-Glow, right here on your shelf, waiting to help *you*. So let's begin, shall we?"

While washing the dishes, Mavis was deciding what dessert to prepare. She'd bought several new ones the day before, and now they all sounded so good she couldn't make up her mind which to use first. The commercial for the canned apple pie ingredients was a little playlet, about a husband coming home at the end of a long hard day, smelling the apple pie, rushing out to the kitchen, sweeping his wife off her feet, kissing her, and saying, "That's my girl!" It sounded promising to Mavis, especially when the announcer said any housewife who got to work right this minute and prepared that apple pie could be almost certain of getting that reaction from her husband.

Then there was a cute jingle from the devil's-food cake mix, sung by a trio of girls' voices with a good swing band in the background. If she'd made the mistake of buying only one box, it said, she ought to go out and buy another before she started baking because one of these luscious devil's-food cakes would not be enough for her hungry family. It was peppy and made Mavis feel better. She checked her shelves and, finding she had only one box, jotted it down on her shopping list.

Next, from the gingerbread mix box, came a homey type commercial that hit Mavis all wrong with its: "MMMMMMM, yes!' Just like Grandmother used to make!"

After listening to several more, she finally decided to use a can of crushed pineapple. "It's quick! It's easy! Yes, Mother, all you do is chill and serve." That was what she needed, feeling the way she did.

She finished the dishes and was just leaving the kitchen when the floor wax bottle called out, "Ladies, look at your floors! You know that others judge you by your floors. Are you proud of yours? Are they ready—spotless and gleaming for the most discerning friend who might drop in?" Mavis looked at her floors. Definitely, they needed attention. She gave them a hasty going over with the quick-drying wax, grateful, as she so often was, to MV for reminding her.

In rapid succession, then, MV announced that now it was possible to polish her silverware to a higher, brighter polish than ever before; wondered if she weren't perhaps guilty of "H.O.—Hair Odour", and shouldn't perhaps wash her hair before her husband came home; told her at three different times to relax with a glass of cola; suggested that she had been neglecting her nails and might profit from a new coat of enamel; asked her to give a thought to her windows; and reminded her that her home permanent neutralizer would lose its wonderful effectiveness the longer it was kept. By early afternoon, she had done the silver and the windows, given herself a shampoo and a manicure, determined to give Kitty a home permanent that very afternoon, and was full of cola. But she was exhausted.

It *was* a responsibility to be the wife of an MV executive. You had to be sort of an example to the rest of the community. Only sometimes she got so tired! Passing the bathroom, she was attracted by a new bottle of pills that Fred had purchased. It was saying, "You know, folks, this is the time of day when you need a lift. Yessir, if you're feeling listless, tired, run down, put some iron back in your backbone! All you do is take off my top, take out one tablet, swallow it, and feel your strength return!" Mavis was about to do so when an aspirin bottle called out, "I go to work instantly!" and then another aspirin bottle (Why *did* Fred keep buying new ones before they'd finished up the old one? It made things so confusing!) said, "I go to work twice as fast!" Aspirin, Mavis suddenly realized, was what she needed. She had a splitting headache, but heavens, how did one know which to take? One of each seemed the only fair solution.

When the children came home from school, Kitty refused to have her hair permanented until her mother took her to the store, as promised. Mavis felt almost unable to face it. What was it Grandmother used to call their supermarket? Hell on earth, hell on wheels, something like that. Mavis, of course, understood that simultaneous MV messages were necessary in the stores in order to give every product a chance at its share of the consumer dollar, but just this afternoon she did wish she could skip it.

Having promised, though, there was nothing to do but get it over with. Billy had to come along too, naturally—both the children loved visiting the supermarket more than most anything else. They made their way down the aisles through a chorus of "Try me . . . Try me. . . . Here is the newer, creamier Mother, your children will. . . . Kiddies, ask Mom to pick the bright green and red package. . . . Here I am, right here, the shortening all your friends have been telling you about. . . ."

Billy listened to as many as he could while they were passing by, and for the thousandth time wished that he could hear the store-type commercials at home. Why, some of them were just as good as the home-type! He always tried to talk the supermarket checkers out of tearing off the Buy-Me-Discs, but they always grumbled that them was their orders and they didn't have no time to bother with him. That was one of the reasons Billy had long since decided to be a supermarket checker himself when he grew up. Think of it! Not only would you hear the swell home-type commercials all day while you worked, and be hep to the very latest ones, but you'd get to hear all the store commercials too. And what with the thousands of Buy-Me-Discs he'd be tearing off, as a Checker, he bet he could slip some into his pockets from time to time, and then wouldn't his friends envy him, being able to receive store-type commercials at home!

They reached the cereal area, and as always the children were entranced. Their faces shone with excitement as they picked up one box after another, to hear the commercials more clearly. There were sounds of gunfire, all kinds of snapping, crackling, and popping; there were loud shouts of "CRISPIER! NUTTIER! YUMMIER!" There were more modulated appeals, addressed to Mother, about increased nourishment and energy-building; there were the voices of athletes, urging the kids to come on and be one of the gang; there were whinnies of horses and explosive sounds of jets and rockets; there were cowboy songs and hillbilly songs and rhymes and jingles and bands and quartets and trios! Poor Kitty! How could she ever choose?

247

Mavis waited patiently for twenty minutes, enjoying the children's pleasure even though her headache was growing worse, and then told Kitty that she really must make up her mind.

"OK, Mom, I'll take this one this time," said Kitty. She held the box close to her mother's ear. "Listen to it, Mom; isn't it swell?" Mavis heard a shattering command, "FORWARD, MARCH!" and then what sounded like a thousand marching men. "Crunch, crunch, crunch, crunch," they were shouting in unison, above the noise of their marching feet, and a male chorus was singing something about Crunchies were marching to your breakfast table, right into your cereal bowl. Suddenly, inexplicably, Mavis felt she couldn't stand this every morning. "No, Kitty," she said, rather harshly, "you can't have that one. I won't have all that marching and shouting at breakfast!" Kitty's pretty face turned to a thundercloud, and tears sprang into her eyes. "I'll tell Daddy what you said! I'll tell Daddy if you don't let me have it!" Mavis came to her senses as quickly as she had taken leave of them. "I'm sorry, dear, I don't know what came over me. Of course you can have it. It's a very nice one. Now let's hurry on home so we can give you your permanent before Grandmother comes."

Grandmother arrived just in time for dinner. She kissed the children warmly, though they didn't remember her, and seemed glad to see Mavis and Fred. But it soon became clear that she was the same old Grandmother. She tried, at table, to shout above the dinner commercials, until Mavis had to shush her or the family would have missed them, and she nearly succeeded in spoiling their pleasure in the new Tummy's campaign, which they had been eagerly looking forward to for several days.

Fred knew the kids were going to like it. He had a brand new roll of Tummys in his pocket, all ready to receive it. It was nicely timed—just as Fred was finishing his pineapple came a loud and unmistakable belch. The children looked startled and then burst into laughter. Mavis looked shocked, and then joined the laughter as a man's voice said, "Embarrassing, isn't it? Supposing that had been *you*! But what's worse is the distress of suppressing stomach gases. Why risk either the embarrassment or the discomfort? Take a Tummy after each meal and avoid the risk of (the belch was repeated, sending the children into fresh gales of laughter). Yes, folks, be sure it doesn't happen to YOU."

Fred handed Tummys to all of them amidst exclamations from the children, "Gee, Daddy, that's the best yet," and "I can't wait for tomorrow night to hear it again!" Mavis thought it was 'very good, very effective'. Grandmother, however, took her Tummy tablet, dropped it on the floor, and ground it to powder with her foot. Fred and Mavis exchanged despairing glances.

That evening the children were allowed to sit up late so they could talk to their great-grandmother after the MV went off at eleven. They had been told she'd just returned from a 'trip', and when they asked her about it now she made up stories of far-away places where she'd been, where there wasn't any MV. Then she went on, while they grew bored, to tell them stories of her girlhood, before MV was invented, long before, as she said, "that fatal day when the Supreme Court opened the door to MV by deciding that defenceless passengers on buses had to listen to commercials whether they wanted to or not".

"But didn't they *like* to hear the commercials?" Billy asked.

Fred smiled to himself. Sound kid. Sound as a dollar. Grandmother could talk herself cross-eyed, but Billy wouldn't fall for that stuff.

"No," Grandmother said, and she seemed very sad, "they didn't like them." She made a visible effort to pull herself together. "You know, Fred, the liquor business is missing a big opportunity. Why, if there were a bottle of Old Overholt here right now, saying, 'Drink me, drink me', I'd do it!"

Fred took the hint and mixed three nightcaps.

"As a matter of fact," Mavis said, looking proudly at her husband, "Fred can claim a lot of the credit for that. All those liquor companies begged and pleaded with him for time, offered piles of money and everything, but Fred didn't think it would be a good influence in the home, having bottles around telling you to drink them, and I think he's right. He turned down a whole lot of money!"

"That was indeed splendid of Fred. I congratulate him." Grandmother drank her drink thirstily and looked at her watch. "We'd all better get to bed. You look tired, Mavis, and one must, I assume, especially in this household, be up with the MV in the morning."

"Oh yes, we usually are, and tomorrow," Mavis said excitedly, "Fred has a wonderful surprise for us. Some big new account he's gotten and he won't tell us what it is, but it's going to start tomorrow."

Next morning as the Bascoms and Grandmother were sitting down to breakfast there was a loud knock at the door.

"That's it!" shouted Fred. "Come on, everybody!"

They all ran to the door and Fred threw it open. Nobody was there, but a copy of the New York *Times* was lying on the doorstep, saying:

"Good morning. This is your New York *Times*! Wouldn't you like to have me delivered to your door *every* morning? Think of the added convenience, the added . . ." Mavis pulled Fred out on to the lawn where he could hear her. "Fred!" she cried, "the New York *Times*—you sold the New York *Times*! However did you do it?"

The children crowded around, congratulating him. "Gosh, Dad, that's really something. Did that knocking come right with the message?"

"Yep," said Fred with justifiable pride, "it's part of the message. Look, Mavis," he waved his hand up and down the street. In both directions, as far as they could see, families were clustered around their front doors, listening to New York *Timeses*.

When it was over, the nearer neighbours shouted, "That your idea, Fred?"

"'Fraid I'll have to admit it is," Fred called back, laughing.

From all sides came cries of "Great work, Fred," and "Swell stuff, Fred," and "Say, you sure are on the ball, Fred." Probably only he and Mavis, though, fully realized what it was going to mean in terms of promotion.

Unnoticed, Grandmother had gone into the house into her room, and extracted a small box from one of her suit-cases. Now she came out of the house again and crossed to the family group on the lawn.

"While you're out here where we can talk, I've something to tell you. It might be better if you sent the children into the house."

Mavis asked Kitty if she weren't afraid of missing her new Crunchies commercial, and the children raced inside.

"I can't stand another day of it," Grandmother said. "I'm sorry, but I've got to leave right now."

"Why, Grandmother, you can't—you don't even know where you're going!"

"Oh, I do know where I'm going. I'm going back to jail. It's really the only sensible place for me. I have friends there, and it's the quietest place I know."

"But you can't . . ." Fred began.

"But I can," Grandmother replied. She opened her hand and showed them the little box.

"Earplugs! Grandmother! Put them out of sight, quickly. Wherever did you get them?"

Grandmother ignored Mavis's question. "I'm going to telephone the police and ask them to come and get me." She turned and started into the house.

"She can't do that," Fred said wildly.

"Let her go, Fred. She's right, and besides it solves the whole problem."

"But, Mavis, if she calls the police here it'll be all over the town. I'll be ruined! Stop her and tell her we'll drive her to some other police station!"

Mavis reached her grandmother before Grandmother reached the police, and explained Fred's predicament. A wicked gleam appeared in Grandmother's eye, but it was gone in a second. She looked at Mavis with some tenderness and said all right, just as long as she got back to the penitentiary as quickly as possible.

They all had breakfast. The children, humming the new Crunchies song, marched off to school—they would be told at night that Grandmother had suddenly gone on another 'trip'—and Mavis and Fred drove to a town fifty miles away, with Grandmother and her luggage in the back seat. Grandmother was happy and at peace, thinking, as she listened to the gas tanks yelling to be filled up, the spark plugs crying to be cleaned, and all the other parts asking to be checked, or repaired, or replaced, that she was hearing MV for the last time.

But as the Bascoms were driving back home, after depositing Grandmother, it hit Fred all of a sudden. He fairly shouted in his excitement. "Mavis! We've all been blind as bats!"

"How do you mean, dear?"

"Blind, I tell you, blind! I've been thinking about Grand-mother in prison, and all the thousands of people in jail and prison, *without MV*. They don't buy any products, so they don't get any MV. Can you imagine what that does to their buying habits?"

"Yes, you're right, Fred—five or ten or twenty years with-out it, they probably wouldn't *have* any buying habits after all that time." She laughed. "But I don't see what you can do about it."

"Plenty, Mavis, and not just about prisons. This is going to revolutionize the Corporation! Do you realize that ever since MV was invented we've just assumed that the discs had to be right with the products? Why? In the name of heaven, why? Take a prison, for instance. Why couldn't we, say, have a little box in each cell where the discs could be kept, and that way the prisoners could still hear the MV and it would sort of preserve their buying habits and then when they got out they wouldn't be floundering around?"

"I wonder, Fred, about the prison authorities. You'd have to get their co-operation, I mean they'd have to distribute the discs, wouldn't they?"

Fred was way ahead of her. "We make it a public service, Mavis. Besides the regular MV, we get a few sponsors with vision, some of those big utilities people that like to do good, and they'll be satisfied with just a short plug for their product and then the rest of the message can be for the benefit of the prisoners, like little talks on honesty is the best policy and how we expect them to behave when they get out of jail—things that'll really help prepare them for life on the outside again."

Impulsively, Mavis put her hand on his arm and squeezed it. No wonder she was so proud of her Fred! Who but Fred —Mavis blinked to keep back the tears—who but Fred would think right off, first thing, not just of the money-making side, but of the welfare and betterment of all those poor prisoners!

THESE ARE PAN BOOKS

Weldon Hill

ONIONHEAD

Recently filmed by Warner Bros, starring Andy Griffith, this up-roarious American best-seller, full of meaty humour, will keep you laughing all night. 'Very funny, very sweet.'—*Daily Express*. 'Will shock and sell like hot cakes.'—*Bristol Evening World*. (*Available May,* 1959.)   (3/6)

Patrick Dennis

AUNTIE MAME

American best-seller about the escapades of a rebellious heiress. Now a Warner Bros film starring Rosalind Russell and Forrest Tucker. 'The funniest story about the most unforgettable character you'll ever run across.'—*Chicago Tribune*.   (2/6)

Edwin O'Connor

THE ORACLE

A savage story of American commercial radio by the author of *The Last Hurrah*. Five nights a week five million listeners tuned in to Usher, the man whose lush, optimistic tones and loyal confidence in the 'little man' the world over invariably sent them to bed with re-newed confidence and peace of soul. But was this oracle a phoney and a humbug? 'Fine full-blooded satire.'—*Star*.   (2/6)

Sloan Wilson

THE MAN IN THE GREY FLANNEL SUIT

The American best-seller which has been translated into every lan-guage and was the basis of the recent 20th Century-Fox film, starring Gregory Peck and Jennifer Jones. It is the story of Tom Rath, who found the problems of peace as hard to combat as the horrors of war.   (2/6)

PICK OF THE PAPERBACKS

THESE ARE PAN BOOKS —

Erskine Caldwell

GRETTA

Gretta was a beautiful woman, but she was lonely—and she needed love. For her it had become a drug, and insatiable craving. Even the love of a husband could not hold her—for Gretta was a woman with an obsession. (2/6)

Erskine Caldwell

JOURNEYMAN

The story of a rascal with a gift of the gab, an eye for women and a taste for liquor!—and of the devilish way he came to prey on the folks in Rocky Comfort. (2/6)

Erskine Caldwell

PLACE CALLED ESTHERVILLE

This powerful, earthy story tells of a Negro brother and sister in a Southern town of the US, and of the racial and social barriers that confronted them, turning their lives into a terrifying ordeal. (2/6)

Erskine Caldwell

TOBACCO ROAD

Ribald and rumbustious, written with passionate conviction, it is the story of a doomed people fated to starve because the land is no longer fertile. '*Tobacco Road* is strong meat.'—*Saturday Review*. (2/6)

PICK OF THE PAPERBACKS

Ellery Queen

THE VIRGIN HEIRESSES

We proudly announce this nightmare tale of blackmail, attempted murder and double-dealing as the first PAN title by the world-famous E.Q.   (2/6)

Jonathan Latimer

LADY IN THE MORGUE

Latimer fans will love this new title by the author of *Sinners and Shrouds*. Private detective William Crane juggles with the identity of a dead blonde, cutting grim mortuary capers over a volcano of violence.   (2/6)

Erle Stanley Gardner

THE CASE OF THE FIERY FINGERS

The toughest, most complicated web of intrigue that Perry Mason ever had to fight his way through.   (2/6)

Morris West

THE BIG STORY

Exciting suspense-thriller of a journalist whose story can overthrow a corrupt Italian politician. 'Gripping tale with tense climax.'—*Evening Standard*.   (2/6)

THESE ARE 🐾 PAN BOOKS

Konrad Z. Lorenz

MAN MEETS DOG

Here is a dog book with a difference—full of entertaining stories and reflections, amusingly told. But Doctor Lorenz, whose career has brought him world fame as a scientist, delves deeper. He raises the value and importance of this book to a level reached by only one other —his famous *King Solomon's Ring* (also a PAN book).   (2/6)

The Christophers

DO-IT-YOURSELF

It's smart—it's fun to save money by doing it yourself. A complete book for the home handyman on repairing walls and ceilings, paperhanging, painting (indoors and out), plumbing, draughts, smoking chimneys, fuses, woodworm and dry rot, damp walls, window glazing, etc., covering the floors, hanging curtains. The finest guide for the amateur available at the price. *Illustrated with diagrams*.   (2/6)

L. W. Burgess

THE PAN BOOK OF CROSSWORDS

A book of really popular puzzles, arranged in four sections carefully graded to suit your skill by today's foremost creator of crosswords. Anyone can do them—there are no tricks, no need for a dictionary or reference book.   (2/6)

Robert H. Thouless

STRAIGHT AND CROOKED THINKING

This practical book by an eminent psychologist tells you how to think clearly and avoid muddled reasoning. It exposes many dishonest tricks that are frequently used in argument, drawing the examples from controversial subjects which are often discussed today.   (2/6)

PICK OF THE PAPERBACKS